THE
FOREMAN'S MANUAL

A guide to Building Supervision

By

E. CARRAN
A.I.A.S.
Registered Architect
Incorporated Quantity Surveyor

WITH 172 LINE DIAGRAMS
DRAWN BY THE AUTHOR

SECOND EDITION
REVISED AND ENLARGED

LONDON
CROSBY LOCKWOOD & SON, LTD
26 OLD BROMPTON ROAD, S.W.7

Printed in Great Britain
by Butler & Tanner Ltd., Frome and London

CONTENTS

PREFACE TO THE SECOND EDITION

IT MUST always be a pleasant occupation to write a preface to a second edition to one of your own books, not from vanity alone (although frail Man, being what he is, this creeps in) but because it proves that your work has helped your fellow workers: that it is wanted.

The first edition of *The Foreman's Manual* was very well received by the technical press as a whole, with the exception of two reviewers who not so much criticised my book as tried to browbeat me.

My publishers and myself are of the opinion that a comprehensive chapter on Reinforced Concrete and Prestressed Concrete should be added, whilst the original text, with corrections and slight emendations here and there, remains to all intents and purposes unaltered.

I would forestall the critics who hastily protest that it is impossible to deal with two such vast and profound subjects in a single chapter supplemented by a few elementary diagrams. It is and no attempt has been made to do so.

The chapter has been written solely from the intelligent foreman's point of view. It explains the physical and technical differences between steelwork, reinforced concrete and prestressed concrete so that a cohesive idea of the whole subject is presented to the reader.

The principles of prestressed concrete are extremely complicated and difficult to grasp, in that the 'whys and wherefores', how it differs from normal reinforced concrete, and (most of all) why and how it holds up are not nearly so easy to understand as, say, the structural value of a steel girder or roof truss of which their external appearance alone gives an idea of their physical properties.

The drawings of a prestressed beam are mystifying with the accompanying notes of anchorages, cleats, cables, strands, bars, spiral reinforcement, cable ducts and grouting.

The whole subject of reinforced concrete and prestressed concrete is still (despite the tremendous advances of recent years) only scratched on the surface. It would be futile to pretend that one short chapter could be anything more than a passing word of introduction to certain practical applications on the site, with the main reasons underlying these applications outlined. I claim nothing else for this chapter.

I have read in certain manuals and books what purports to be an explanation of reinforced and prestressed practice for site use, but in fact have found the information useless. They appear to be nothing but voluminous glimpses of the obvious; things which might apply to any building or engineering works, and have no real reference to the understanding of the subject matter. Instructions such as, 'you can saw off the end of the bar with a *hacksaw*', 'thoroughly clean ends of threaded bar with a *wire brush*'. The writer is not content to call a tap on a grout pump a 'tap'. No. It has got to be a '*control* tap'. All this verbiage clutters up the mind, and in reality tells the reader nothing: but it does fill out the book!

I am well aware that in practice there are many methods and processes of work to be followed, from the storage of cement and aggregates to the construction and fixing of formwork, and the making of test cubes. All this work is of the highest importance and has to be carried out expertly. An experienced foreman knows all the general methods and procedure to be adopted in the day-to-day work of a contract, and does not need instruction in routine trivialities.

Throughout *The Foreman's Manual* I have therefore endeavoured to concentrate more on the intellectual processes and reasoning behind the structural functions of modern building construction.

With the advent of batch mixing and ready-mixed concrete, even the time-honoured slump test is losing its importance. Gone are the piles of sand and gravel, the cement storage shed and the array of mixers. The concrete comes exactly as specified and ready to pour. Thus routine details are gradually losing their importance.

I trust that *The Foreman's Manual* in its revised form will prove as useful as the first edition and that it will give added interest to all those engaged in constructions where reinforced and prestressed concrete are used.

E. CARRAN

Church Preen,
Shrewsbury.
1963.

INTRODUCTION

A FOREMAN is an adult person, neither child nor adolescent student; he may be a young man, but is generally in the middle thirties at least. It follows from this that his need for guidance on the many structural and technical problems which confront him require to be presented in an entirely different manner from that in which the same information would be thought fit for a student or a qualified engineer, architect, or surveyor.

The basis of the information must of necessity be the same for all; that for the student being presented as a series of steps, graduated in difficulty, proceeding from the simple to the complex, while the professional man is shewn a problem, very often of the greatest difficulty with accompanying examples proved by use of higher mathematics, the workings of all intermediate steps being omitted, on the assumption that the professional surveyor or engineer will take this for granted; that he will supply the missing steps in his own mind without any prompting.

To the grown foreman in charge of a job with his men crowding around him and his employers waiting for results, the leisurely progress of the student and the deep investigations of the professional are alike useless; he must have recourse to information which is *immediately* necessary; information which is *not simplified* out of all resemblance to the real thing. On the other hand, it must not be loaded with examples of every possible divergence from the main rules of building construction, engineering, or land surveying, with asides and remarks more suitable to a treatise on physics than foremanship.

A foreman on the job has not the time for studying a book, page after page, however well written and informative. He needs something which (whilst being absolutely accurate) he can translate immediately into lines, plumb bobs, boning rods, right angles and level pegs, then and there, amongst all the hurly burly of scaffolding, dumpers, concrete mixers and sheds.

The increasing complexity of modern building and civil engineering operations together with changes in the manner of presentation in plans, details, bills of quantities, and specifications, all make for further calls on the intelligence and quick apprehension of the foreman. The specification especially, whilst reducing responsibility in some respects, by its great detail and phraseology used, thrusts extra care on the shoulders of the foreman.

It is a disturbing aside, that whilst modern buildings become more box-like in elevation and structure, whilst every element of craftsmanship and ornament is practically eliminated, the whole conception of a building project is simplified to such a degree that it might be "designed" and drafted by an esquimau holding a stump of black chalk between his frozen toes, whilst lolling in the snow and ice with his back against an overturned dog-sled. Materials and methods, on the other hand, have become immensely complicated, due to the wide choice of modern materials.

Nevertheless, despite these changes, the *Basis and Essentials* of modern building and civil engineering are exactly the same as they have always been; the main rules, theories, and practical issues have not changed one iota; they have only become obscured by fresh devices and modes of construction.

To the timid, the uncertain, modern building construction presents a terrifying mass of unending complexity, but to the man who knows what to look for, to the man who can discern the "eye" in the folds of the drapery, the tortuous labyrinth becomes the well-defined path. This book is intended to define the path.

Whilst a foreman is generally a craftsman, above the average in skill and intelligence, his work in a building project lies for the most part in setting out, that is, transferring the ideas of the architect or engineer from the plans and specification to the site, and, once this important preliminary is accomplished, explaining to the individual workmen where and how their particular portion of the work is to be performed, to have a good general grasp of *all* trades, and to be sufficiently conversant with specialist work (such as asphalter, patent flooring, lift installations, sprinkler systems, etc.) to enable a good preparation to be made for them.

A foreman on a modern building site must feel himself confident to carry out all these things. It is true that he has the immediate help of the clerk of works for consultation, and behind him the resident engineer or architect, and finally the chief engineer or architect, but even this complete system of guidance is not sufficient. A foreman who is not self-reliant, who persistently seeks direction on any and every point is very quickly requested to undertake work of lesser importance, where questions of every-day routine will not trouble him so much.

There are many points of construction on a large site which the architect or engineer merely indicates on his plans and sections, expecting that the foreman will supply the details from his own knowledge. As an instance, a subsidiary R.S.J. may be shewn running between two main girders. In actual construction it might be found that the concrete floor (which is intended to sit on the subsidiary R.S.J.) comes in at too high a level to do so.

A knowledgeable and well-trained foreman will not have recourse to the architect for instruction, but will insert steel packing pieces to form a seating on the top flange of the subsidiary R.S.J., or as an alternative will cast a dwarf wall to make up the required height. He will of course put this in his report and will no doubt discuss it with the clerk of works, but at the same time he will consult the latter with the suggestion ready made. A hundred similar small contretemps are to be met with in the course of any major contract: the foreman should be able to deal with them decisively.

A foreman should always "have something in hand". Although he may not be called upon to display the half of his knowledge, his inner confidence will be evident in his every action, especially is this so at the commencement of a job, where decision in setting out, comprehension of the structural mechanics of a building, and a thorough understanding of the main points of a specification count above all else.

The scheme of this book is an attempt to fulfil the foreman's needs in all the points briefly enumerated in this preface, to avoid over simplification or the long drawn out examples and divergences of a students' primer, and equally not to become involved in the deep waters of the specialists' book of reference.

A foreman's duties lie principally in setting out, a good knowledge of the use of the chief surveying instruments, namely the dumpy level and the theodolite, and the main rules governing building mechanics, which might be defined as strength of materials, bending moments, and stresses. This knowledge, allied to a mastery of his own craft, will fit a foreman for great responsibility and the most rigorous tests.

During recent years the foreman has emerged as a person of

considerable importance on all matters to do with building and civil engineering contracts. Employers especially (as exemplified by Masters Builders Associations) are showing in a practical form their appreciation of their foremen's help. The week-end courses, lectures, meetings, and discussions organised by groups of employers, manufacturers, and the foremen themselves give good and clear evidence of the high esteem in which building foremen are now held in the industry, an appreciation seconded by architects, engineers, and surveyors.

The complexities of modern building and civil engineering practice make the foreman's lot an onerous one indeed. May I hope that the information conveyed in this book will help to ease the burden.

E. CARRAN

Church Preen,
Shrewsbury.
1957.

Chapter I

WHAT CONSTITUTES A GOOD FOREMAN?

A FOREMAN should be a craftsman; a man who has mastered his own trade in every detail and who, by his superior intelligence, will-power and energy, has forged ahead of his fellow workers and so fitted himself to handle the reins on a job.

But it takes even more than this to make a good foreman. It demands that indefinable attribute of the human being called "character". Something which cannot be learned from a school, a college, a prospectus, something which cannot be inculcated; it must come from the man himself. Everyone coming into contact with such a man, even if it be only over the smallest technical matter, must be aware of the man's "character", his staunchness, his probity, his uprightness of purpose. If that intangible aura is missing, then that person should not be a foreman on a building job.

"Character" (especially in the broad world of building) is not a thing to be "formed". A man who allows someone to "form his character" for him at once proclaims himself as unstable, devoid of firm principles, a weak-kneed and willing disciple of regimentation; in other words, he is unreliable, he has no will of his own.

To have a set and unshakable individual purpose (based on sound principles) is the prerequisite of a building foreman.

This definition of character does not mean that a man should be inflexible, unwilling to compromise, stubborn in a set course, blind to instruction and to other people's ideas; that is merely being a blockhead. The foreman of character is quite the reverse. He is only too willing to learn, to absorb new ideas, to compromise, to cut his suit according to his cloth, but, having character, he will not carry out new ideas merely because they are "new"; that is not sufficient for an intelligent man.

Allied to the all-important question of character must come the personal characteristics of the man. A foreman must be first of all equable of temper, just in his dealing, strict in discipline

11

(yet not overbearing or officious), sympathetic, and fully alive to his duty to his employers and to the men under his control; above all he must be modest.

It does not matter how clever he may be technically, how adept at his own craft, how wide the range of his experience; nothing puts the men's backs up more than an ostentatious display on the part of the foreman. Such a man is at once branded as a "know-all" by the men and his employers.

An employer, far from being impressed by his foreman's knowledge of the job, objects to being "instructed".

Orderliness, discipline, correct supervision and technical and craft knowledge must flow from the foreman's quiet management without being apparent; it must not come in bugle blasts and staccato orders.

From a mélange of planks, huts, spoil heaps, scaffolding and plant, the completed building should gradually evolve, step by step, in orderly precision, all due to the foreman's smooth management and knowledge brought into play as each stage of the building project is achieved.

This result, and this only, is the mark of good foremanship.

It brings its own reward. The men remain contented and happy, and are the first to appreciate the cleverness and real efficiency of the foreman's guidance; their intelligence has not been insulted at every turn by unnecessary instruction in the simplest aspects of their crafts, the setting out has been accurate and reliable, the commencement and limits of each stage of the work have been indicated to them in a clear manner, and there has been none of that vexatious pulling down of work, that awkward bodging up of levels, that narrowing of door frames to "work in", or diversions of trenches, all of which bespeak the inefficient but oft-times ostentatious foreman.

A good foreman always wins the appreciation of his men and, in fact, has a following; a group of sound craftsmen and labourers who will travel from job to job as necessary.

An employer (whether he be an individual or a company of directors with their managers and under-managers) is usually quick to recognise the merits of a good foreman. While the individual processes of a building contract may not interest an employer (indeed, he may be quite ignorant of them), the final result does, namely the date of completion and the final prime cost. This last especially reveals the efficiency or otherwise of the foreman's supervision, and it is rare indeed for an employer not to recognise this in some substantial form at the successful completion of a contract.

It is a peculiarity of the building and civil engineering world that most foremen are either bricklayers or joiners. Seldom is a plumber, painter, plasterer or electrician to be found in the ranks of the general foremen. Why this should be I do not know, since each craft demands a high degree of intelligence and manual skill.

I have known one navvy who became a foreman, who raised himself literally from the bottom of the trench to the foreman's hut without any intermediate process of "improving" or general odd job work; he graduated by sheer intelligence and force of character. He never made the mistake of pretending to the men that he was a craftsman. He had the facility for smoothing out other men's difficulties and worries, of going to the root of a problem, and more important still, of interpreting plans and setting out in a manner that even the most backward intelligence could grasp; but doubtless this man was an exception.

Most foremen have all sorts of out-of-the-way knowledge apart from their work, knowledge most often of a semi-scientific nature, such as clock making, remedies for coccidiosis, the pollination of fruit trees, an explanation of the gyroscope; one foreman even overwhelmed me with a lengthy dissertation on the theory of relativity.

More rarely a foreman will swing towards the arts, which generally takes the form of music, or sketching for preference.

It would be idle to pretend that the achievements in these outside fields are of a high order; for the most part they are not, but what is important is the fact that it shows a great catholicity of interests apart from the main one by which they earn their living. These wider interests all go to make up the man and are more evident in the building trade than in any other branch of industry or profession.

But enough of generalities. Now for the practical aspects. The contract has been let, and the job is waiting to start.

Do not be in too much of a hurry. "Hasten slowly." Never was a motto more apt for the building trade.

Always remember that you are the foreman in sole charge

from first to last. If anyone should gainsay you and you are tempted (either through timidity or discretion) to step down, at the same moment you are relinquishng all moral hold and command of your job. Be firm! Never mind what the boss's favourite nephew thinks; be deferential but insistent. Your methods and yours alone are the ones to be employed.

This awkward moment occurs sooner or later to every foreman, and many a good man has suffered bitterly through want of suitable guidance. Remember then, in the face of all comers; there is only one foreman, and that is you!

The contract may be of the compact sort, all on one site within comparatively small confines; school, factory, private house, or swimming pool, or it may be large and straggling, a housing scheme, sewerage works and main outfall, or reservoir and extensive pipe lines, manholes and pump houses.

Do not make the mistake of rushing in straight away, loading up a lorry with hut and sleepers and invading the site with a tremendous flourish; you will come to a full stop with your own time and that of four men ticking off against the job.

Demand two full days to study the plans, sections, and details, especially the site plan and specification or blank bills of quantities. When these have been assimilated in a broad manner, visit the job and go over the ground in detail, plan in hand and take notes of the physical peculiarities of the site; that brook there (very dirty and no good for concrete water), the allotments in the way exactly where you would have placed the concrete mixer, the waterlogged ground necessitating a sleeper road, the main road full of heavy traffic abutting the site of a new deep retaining wall, the sprawl of foundation steelwork in the very spot where it would have been most convenient to erect the crane.

Go back and think it over! When you do eventually come on to the site all major difficulties will have been foreseen; the preliminary operations will proceed like clockwork.

The deployment of the foreman's hut, the clerk of works' hut, the cement shed, timekeeper's hut, mess sheds and general stores are the most important moves in the contract. Do not place any of these temporary sheds so that they have to be moved halfway through the job to make room for the permanent works; it shows lack of foresight and does not pass unnoticed.

Once the foreman is settled in, the next most important thing is to establish good relations with the clerk of works. The surest way to do this is to see that he has a comfortable hut properly furnished with a good roadway to it so that the approach is clear from mud, making certain that there is a proper supply of washing and drinking water, heating materials, and a broom. If the terms of the contract call for it, install the telephone immediately.

Let the clerk of works see and feel from the commencement of the job that he is a man of some importance, as a direct representative of the client and an agent of the architect or engineer. An experienced clerk of works will not assume undue importance because of this treatment; he will take it as his due and go about his duties quietly and methodically. Everyone will benefit, and the foreman's efforts to make the clerk of works comfortable (a requirement so often skimped) will redound to his own credit and that of the job itself. Things will run easily from the first, hold-ups and unnecessary telephone calls and letter writing will be reduced to a minimum, and many technical and site difficulties will be dealt with expeditiously as they arise by reason of the absence of friction and the feeling of good will existing between the clerk of works and the foreman.

Before engaging in active conversation with the clerk of works, the wise and experienced foreman will provide himself with a notebook containing two carbon copies. One copy to be sent to head office, one handed to the clerk of works, whilst the remaining sheet will be retained in the foreman's own book. Obvious as this requirement is, it is most important and, moreover, one which is frequently overlooked.

Always have written evidence.

A record in writing of a decision, an extra, a discrepancy, a variation, a point of construction, or an error is the one sure means of placing credit where credit is due; it establishes responsibility and records many an important point which would otherwise become obscured by the time the end of the contract is reached.

Armed with the duplicate book, the plans, details, specification and bills of quantities (in a job of any size the specification is generally a separate document) the contract may be followed through in detail with the clerk of works who will give instructions as to which part of the works is to be commenced first.

Should the nature of the proposed contract demand work to be done out of the usual trade order (possibly a factory where the directors have decided to commence production immediately with certain preliminary processes whilst waiting for the completion of the rest of the buildings) the clerk of works will go very thoroughly into the question at the first meeting, and it is here that the experienced foreman will require to make many notes, especially if the unusual order of the working is likely to lead to unforeseeable expense, an expense not allowed for or intended in the original bills of quantities.

Check and compare the bills of quantities with the specification; it will probably be found that there are a good many discrepancies between the two. Obtain the clerk of work's decision as to which is to be followed, *and confirm it.*

If the instructions entail an extra expense, this must be notified to the architect or engineer at once. Does the specification give spun iron pipes 12ft. long while the quantities give pipes 18ft. long? A very important point. Think of the extra lead joints. Does one document specify "Class B" while the other demands "Class C?" Follow through the levels. Note if the quantities specify depth to bottom of trenches while the drawings and specification give the same depths to invert of pipes. Are the steel window heights in complete conformity with the half-inch details, and have the oak surrounds been allowed for? Have lightweight manhole covers been specified for the middle of the road where extremely heavy traffic may be expected? Do main stanchions come up surprisingly through the middle of half landings? How will the narrow gauge facing bricks course in with the common backing, the artificial stone surrounds and the mahogany frames? Is there sufficient working space between the new reinforced concrete retaining wall and the existing property to allow for the spreading of the vertical asphalt damp-proof course?

All these and a hundred similar questions will occur on the various contracts, and must be dealt with and agreed upon by the clerk of works and the foreman at the earliest possible moment. These are the routine difficulties of all jobs. It is surprising what ill will is engendered, what subterfuge is resorted to if such questions are not dealt with in a straightforward and methodical manner from the commencement of the works.

One thing leads to another. The inspection of the plans and the elucidation of the various points with the clerk of works often has a secondary use of great value to the foreman, namely, the ordering of materials. Most large contractors these days have a special department at head office for the ordering of materials: The surveyors so employed are supposed to foresee and order all necessary materials well in advance of the required date for use. This relieves the pressure on the foreman considerably, but nevertheless a shrewd reminder to head office about materials from the man actually on the job is always much appreciated, and in many instances is of considerably more use than mere dry office work. There is one danger to guard against in this connection: duplication of orders.

In a contract of an extensive nature there should be a separate time office whether the men are booked by time sheets, time book, or tokens. It is not necessary for the foreman to be present all the time while the men arrive or leave the job; this should be the duty of an efficient time and materials clerk. The foreman should, however, pay occasional and unexpected visits.

All daywork should be adequately described on daywork sheets (even though the men may be checked in by token) and passed to the clerk of works to sign each day, or alternatively the sheets may be written up in a special book, each job being described under its proper heading.

The rules governing the acceptance of daywork on a contract must be scrupulously observed, and no attempt made to work in part of the general contract. These tactics gain nothing under an astute clerk of works—quite to the contrary. They lead to friction and cast suspicion on all future work of a daywork nature.

It would, of course, be a reasonable and correct thing to charge, for instance, cartage, unloading, and even setting out, where all these separate services are involved with ordinary contract work, providing a proper proportion is allocated to daywork and the attention of the clerk of works drawn to this.

A six-ton load of cement with special cartage from some distant depot might have one ton for use in daywork, in which case it would be fair and reasonable to charge one-sixth of the special cartage charges together with the amount for loading. A whole day might be spent in levelling and setting out a portion of the site including items carried out under daywork. Here again, it would be reasonable to charge a certain portion of this time to daywork.

There are certain general duties which fall to the lot of the foreman, not the least of which is keeping a knowledgeable watch on the quality and quantity of the materials delivered on the job by the various suppliers and merchants, amongst which sand and gravel, pitching and aggregates of all kinds takes a very prominent place. This is especially important on an extensive concrete job.

WATCH THE SAND AND GRAVEL!

Where sand and aggregate are sold by the yard cube, instruct the carpenter to build two bins, each containing exactly three or four yards cube as convenient, with calibrated numbers painted on the sides in large black characters. Tip odd loads into these bins throughout the course of the job.

Where sand and aggregates are sold by the ton, insist on a public weighbridge ticket and take particular note of the water content or of old motor-car tyres or wooden boxes left in the wagon and covered up by the sand or gravel. Human nature being what it is, such things require firm remonstrance.

The next minor point is the giving of notices to local and county authorities.

Statutory notices are generally three in number: Notice of intention to Commence Building, Drains and Foundation Inspection, and Completion. Scrupulously give these notices in on their due dates, and all will be well. (Some Councils may require seven.)

Finally, keep a concise day to day diary of the job, noting the weather in particular, when rained off, architects' or engineers' visits, with special mention of verbal orders which might have been given when walking round the job.

One last word. Because there have been discrepancies between the plans and the bills of quantities, and further points of disagreement between the bills of quantities and the specification, do not make the mistake of thinking that the architect or engineer does not know his job; he does! An intelligent query about an error is appreciated by the architect concerned, whereas a conceited announcement or the suggestion that the engineer is incompetent, engenders bad feeling. It is not helpful to the job.

If the psychological groundwork is sound, if the foreman

possesses those traits of character outlined in this chapter, if the preliminaries are well thought out, nothing can mar the practical work of building which follows.

Chapter II

SETTING OUT BUILDING WORKS

IT is one thing to look at and understand a plan of a building drawn to a scale of $\frac{1}{8}$in. to a foot or, as in the case of some engineering undertakings, 500 feet to a foot; it is quite a different matter to walk on to a building site and proceed to translate what is indicated on the plans into the actual size of the building.

In the first place every line and dimension on the plan is magnified 96 times and in the second example it is enlarged 500 times.

Most things appear totally different under magnification; building works are no exception to this phenomenon.

What appeared to be easy and straightforward on the one-eighth scale drawings on the job appears to be an impossibility; the ground rises steeply so that a level line is out of the question, a building is in the way of an important offset, and what appeared to be a little brook on the 1/500th layout now turns out to be a swift running river 30ft. wide with steep banks covered with bracken.

The agent or foreman who has thoroughly mastered the art of setting out will be undismayed by whatever obstacles the site places in his way. He will have confidence in himself and the instruments he uses, he will commence his work with certainty knowing exactly where he is and, what is equally important, where he will end. All questions of levels, gradients, inverts, curves and boundaries will be clear-cut, new works will tie in precisely with existing buildings, steelwork construction and reinforcement will fall into place without trouble, and frames, canopies and specialist items will slide into their allotted openings without that vexatious cutting and shifting and pinching which so often accompanies these operations.

The basis of all setting out is THE BASE LINE: lay this straight and true, place it exactly on the ground as it is shown on the plan and half the job is accomplished; all difficulties vanish.

On large jobs, such as bridges, tunnels, railways, canals, where a chosen base line might be anything from half-a-mile to five miles long, untold trouble is expended on its exact measurement. Anything from three to six months is taken up in readings of the line under all temperatures and conditions of weather, during heat and cold, during sunlight and night time. Every factor which might govern the length of the line is recorded; pull on the tape, sag, temperature expansion and contraction and, of course, arithmetical rectifications for slope of ground; dozens of readings are taken, analysed and then averaged.

No such precautions are necessary in the general run of building works, but this example serves to show the importance of the base line.

The base line in small works may be an actual measured line in a field, defined by pegs, or it may be a hedge, a road kerb, or even the wall of an existing house. Whatever the base line is, go through all operations thoroughly of exact measurement and direction. All offsets must be taken from this and referred back to it.

A builder does not require the same knowledge of instruments that the engineer and surveyor require. These men use their knowledge to plot and draw the characteristics of a site and finally to design constructions to fit that site, their ideas and intentions being conveyed to the contractor in the form of plans, sections, elevations and specifications.

The building contractor, on the other hand, has nothing whatever to do with this process in the erection of a building or engineering undertaking. He need not know the shape, direction and extent of a piece of land or of the proposed buildings on it. All this is done for him by the engineer or architect and drawn to scale on the plans given to him, from which he can carry out the work as intended.

The engineer and architect use surveying instruments in order to obtain a true plan and contours of a site.

The contractor uses his surveying instruments in order to be able to place the required buildings and works on the site.

An engineer reduces his survey figures to, say, 1/500th of their real size and draws it on a plan. The contractor, on the other hand, enlarges his figures by 500 times and plots these dimensions on the actual ground.

A builder only needs sufficient knowledge of surveying instruments in order to allow him to carry out the work defined; beyond this he need not go; the detailed knowledge and formulæ of the engineer and land surveyor are totally unnecessary.

The simple method should always be chosen in preference to the complicated.

Before even a peg can be driven or a line stretched the need of a reliable square makes itself felt; the bulk of all setting out is the right angle.

The square is best made in the shop by a skilled joiner, set out on the bench and planed and trued up to the greatest degree of accuracy possible. For preference use oak and make each arm of the square 4ft. long at least: you then have a reliable means of setting out right angles which will last a lifetime. Too often the square is a rough and ready piece of work knocked up on the job out of any old pieces of deal lying about, the use of which leads to much shifting of pegs and adjustments when the diagonals come to be checked. It cannot be stressed too strongly that the builder's square should be a first-class piece of joinery with sharp arrises along which the line can be stretched with great accuracy.

In an emergency a true right angle may be set up by the simple process of marking out a triangle in the ratio of 3: 4: 5, this last being the hypotenuse. Again we are indebted to Pythagorus, who was kind enough to point out to the world that the square on the hypotenuse equals the sum of the squares on the other two sides; hence $3^2 + 4^2 = 5^2$.

Never undertake the setting out of any work, however simple, without a good supply of stout sawn pegs. A selection should be taken along from 3ft. $\times$ 2in. $\times$ 2in. up to 6ft. stakes 3in. $\times$ 3in. square.

All main pegs, offset points and level pegs should be driven well in and concreted. You then have a reliable reference for all future measurements and levels without the likelihood of the pegs having been shifted by mischievous children, kicked over by cattle or knocked sideways by the wheel of a lorry.

Before embarking on the actual business of setting out, thoroughly check all measurements on the plans, making certain that the external wall measurements are the exact total of the intermediate dimensions, including the thickness of the walls. A frequent error is the omission of the thickness of one or more cross walls with the result that the placing of door, window and passage openings when added to the distance between openings, differs by multiples of 4½in., 9in. or 14in., as the case may be. Should any such discrepancy be found it is a great saving of time to check over the internal and cross walls and partitions.

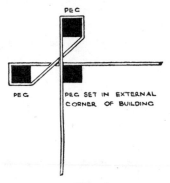

FIG. 1

You can now drive the first peg. Set it squarely in the external corner of the building as indicated in Fig. 1. See that it is vertical and then set another peg at the end of the line. Stretch a line between the two pegs, fairly taut and level. Next lay the builder's square with one leg pointing along the line when two extension pegs can now be driven, as shown in Fig. 1, the line looped around them and carefully laid in true alignment with the other leg of the square. This operation sets out two main walls at right angles. When all the main lines are complete test for accuracy by reading the diagonals with a tape. The readings should, of course, be the same. If there is any discrepancy test each corner for squareness, when the offending pegs will soon be discovered.

It often happens that the setting out has to be done on a bank or steeply sloping site while the actual footings are perhaps 5ft. or 6ft. down. This is shown in Fig. 2 when it will be seen how important it is to have a true sawn peg and to be absolutely certain which side of the line you are plumbing from.

In the average house or small construction the latter point has not very much importance, but in the case of a steel frame building where there is a line of stanchions, the centres of which do not coincide with the centre line of the wall, it is very important to plumb accurately from the correct side of the line. In setting out always follow the same routine.

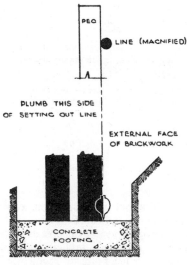

FIG. 2

In larger and more complicated jobs the corner pegs may be replaced with profiles, as shown in Fig. 3. Each wall has its own profile on which is marked (by means of painted stripes) the main wall thickness, plinth, footing offsets and total width of concrete footing. Fine saw cuts may be made in the profile at these points and the line notched through for setting out each part of the work in succession. This is a very good method but is not called for in works of a simple nature.

As to tapes, a linen tape 100ft. long is the most useful for building works; it is light in weight, easily cleaned and easily manipulated. It has the disadvantage of being very prone to stretching, which makes dimensions register shorter than they actually are. This is not a very serious matter in itself for small works but leads to trouble in specialist work which has been prepared away from the job and has to be fitted in. As an example, a 100ft. tape which has stretched 2in. will measure a recess 100ft. long as 99ft. 10in., which will be the dimension to be passed on to the specialist firm to make whatever fitment specified. The manufacturer will no doubt set his work out to 99ft. 10in. by means of a steel tape.

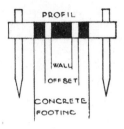

FIG. 3

For this reason all large works, such as steelwork constructions and machine bases, should be set out by means of a steel tape.

Steel tapes always break 15 minutes before knocking off time when you are completing the setting out for the next day's work. They also invariably snap at a point which prohibits the taking of an important tie.

Work in long grass or over rough ground requires the use of a steel chain, of which there are two sorts: the Gunter's Chain, which is 66ft. in length, and the Engineer's Chain, which is 100ft. in length. Each chain is divided into 100 links; the Gunter link is 7·92in. whilst the Engineer's is 12in. in length.

For building and engineering works the engineer's chain only should be used, the Gunter's chain being restricted to the land surveyor.

The chain is read by means of brass tallies fastened at 10ft. intervals along its length. The first tally to look for is the central, or 50ft., mark, as shown in Fig. 4: a simple flat, round tongue.

Since the chain is read from either the back or forward station it is important to look for the 50ft. tally first of all. A distance of 10ft. is indicated by a brass tally with one point, a distance of 20ft. by a tally with two points, and so on up to 40ft., as shown in Fig. 5.

CENTRE TALLY

50 FEET

FIG. 4

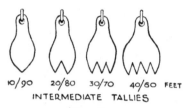

10/90   20/80   30/70   40/60 FEET

INTERMEDIATE TALLIES

FIG. 5

Because the chain may be read from either station each tally has two values.

The single point thus has a value of either 10ft. or 90ft., the double point indicates either 20ft. or 80ft. according to its position with reference to the centre tally and the end from which the readings have been commenced. This peculiarity is one to which you soon become accustomed. It should be noted that all measurements are taken from the very end of the brass swivel handle shown in Fig. 6.

There is one practical point worth knowing in the management of chains; how to undo the chain and how to coil it up again after use. It is not necessary to fight it or wrestle with it or try to emulate the late Mr. Houdini.

Undo the leather strap and place (not throw) the chain, bundled up as it is, on the ground. Pick out the central tally (which is easily distinguished) and, holding the tag in the right hand, walk away with the chain which will draw itself out in a double 50ft. line; lay down the chain, walk round to one of the brass handles and pull out straight, when the chain is ready for use.

To pack up the chain neatly, pick up the chain by the central tag once more and draw it out until the chain folds itself together bringing the links together with the left hand and grasping them with the right as you do. The chain will automatically come together in a neat bundle ready for use the next time.

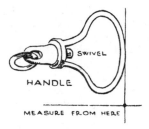

SWIVEL

HANDLE

MEASURE FROM HERE

FIG. 6

Along with the chain goes a set of 10 steel arrows which can be set conveniently in the ground every full 100ft. or any intermediate part or multiple of 100ft. The arrows should each have a piece of bright red material knotted around the top to enable them to be easily discerned in tall grass.

Make a rule (even for short distances) always to carry the full complement of 10 arrows. The forward chainman places them as he goes along while the rear chainman (who has started off with no arrows) picks them up as he progresses. When the line is finally measured, the number of arrows held by the rear chainman plus any measured fractions of 100ft. should represent the number of "100fts." measured which together with the fraction gives the true length of the line. Similarly the number of arrows left in the hand of the forward chainman deducted from the 10 arrows plus the fraction should give a like result. A full set of arrows so used is an excellent check over long distances.

A set of ranging rods (at least six) is absolutely essential. Simple as these things are, it is useful to know a few facts about them.

Many a time it is these ordinary out-of-the-way snatches of knowledge which save the day should any unforeseen event occur.

Ranging poles are made in lengths varying from 6ft. to 12ft. increasing by 2ft. intervals. They are enamelled in sections coloured black, white and red, each section being 12in. long, but sometimes the sections are in links, namely 7·92in., so beware if you are using a ranging rod for quick offset measurements.

A very useful adjunct to a set of ranging rods is a metal bracket which enables the rods to be set upright on an existing concrete road, or, what is more important, to be set up on hard shale or rock where the ironshod point would not otherwise enter. The same supports are so devised that the pole may be clamped upright on sloping ground.

In work of any size it is seldom that the setting out can be used directly from the main lines, due in many cases to the fact that while the lines have been set on the ground before it is dug, the actual work may be at a depth of 10ft. or 15ft., consequently all main positions and points must be plumbed down, especially where work in the basement has to coincide with extreme accuracy with the construction above ground. This matter has already been touched on, but our previous remarks require amplification.

For work of this nature it is not advisable to use a bricklayer's plumb rod with horizontal levels as is so popular to-day, or even the old-fashioned plumb bob where a weight of lead is suspended from a string which coincides with a centre line marked down the board.

There is only one certain and accurate method for plumbing from a height: the turned brass plummet with a steel point freely hanging from a cord, held in the hand or notched over a cross bar.

The free hanging plummet gives a truly vertical line by reason of the fact that it is obeying the natural law of gravity, which is to pull the metal object immediately to the centre of the earth, but the hand, holding the other end of the cord to which the plummet is attached, prevents the plummet from falling, and so, between the two forces of gravity and the resistance of your hand, the line is pulled taut and truly vertical as explained in Fig. 7.

What the layman calls vertical is really a line radiating from the centre of the earth, and what is understood by level is a line tangential to the surface of the earth and at right angles to the vertical line or radius.

A bricklayer's plumb bob with horizontal bubbles, while quite accurate for coursing brickwork and testing small heights, may

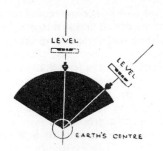

FIG. 7

contain errors of setting (very difficult to detect) as shown in Fig. 8 where the effect is greatly exaggerated. It will be appreciated that such an error in a small height would be negligible but becomes very important as the height increases.

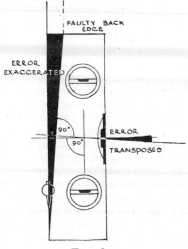

FIG. 8

The optical square (never was a name better chosen) is one of the most useful little instruments for the quick setting out of right angles both for general survey work and for actual building operations. It is not to be recommended for the setting out of buildings, but is of inestimable value for long lines of fencing, boundary walls, sewers, water mains, or taking offsets from base lines.

The instrument consists of a small circular box about 4½in. diameter, made of brass, gunmetal, or bronze, and containing two mirrors set at 45 deg. to each other. One of the mirrors is completely silvered as shown in Fig. 9, while the other is silvered only in the bottom half, the top half consisting of clear glass, so that a direct view as through a window is obtained. The mirror is shown in Fig. 9.

An object placed beyond this mirror can, therefore, be clearly seen (or rather a small portion of it, sufficient to indicate its direction).

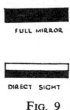

FULL MIRROR

DIRECT SIGHT

FIG. 9

Two ranging poles and an assistant are needed to set out a right angle as shown in Fig. 9a.

The procedure is simple. A ranging pole is set up at one end of the line from which it is desired to construct the right angle; a peg is driven in on the line at the exact point of departure and the optical square is centred over this spot while the surveyor looks towards the ranging rod, bringing it into view through the upper and unsilvered portion of the mirror. The assistant in the meanwhile has taken the second ranging rod and stands with it (held well away from his body) in a position which appears to be at right angles with the base line. This generally gives a non-coincident image as indicated in Fig. 10. The surveyor then gives signals to his assistant by means of a full arm wave until the second ranging pole coincides exactly with the top half of the first ranging pole as shown in Fig. 10 when the operation is complete.

The theory of the optical square is very neat and depends for its accuracy on the well-known fact that a ray of light from an object reflected in a flat ground mirror will bounce back, as it were, at the same angle as it entered the surface of the mirror.

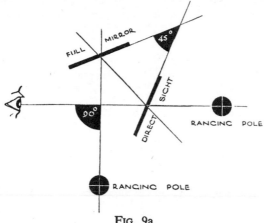

FIG. 9a

Thus, in Fig. 9a, the ray of light from the second or offset ranging pole strikes the full mirror at an angle of 67½ deg. and, therefore, bounces off at the same angle, namely 67½ deg.

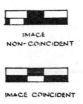

FIG. 10

Euclid has demonstrated and proved that if two straight lines meet another straight line, the included angles together equal 180 deg. so that, looking at Fig. 9a once more, and noting the direction of the rays and the angles formed thereby in the full mirror we have the simple addition 67½ deg. + 67½ deg. + 45 deg. = 180 deg. It is the last angle of 45 deg. which brings the reflected image of the offset pole bang on to the line of sight, making the two poles appear as one.

There are no lenses or focusing in an optical square, so that for this reason alone offsets at a distance are not too reliable.

Another useful device for setting out right angles is the cross head. (It will also set out angles at 45 deg.)

FIG. 11

This little instrument was much in vogue about fifty years ago, but it seems to have gone out of fashion to-day. It is indicated in Fig. 11 where its method of use is at once apparent. The staff, carrying a threaded head is fixed in the ground on the exact centre from which it is desired to set off the angle. The staff is set truly vertical by means of a plummet, the cross head screwed on, and a sight taken through the appropriate eye slit to a ranging rod held by an assistant who moves it to one side or the other until it is exactly centred through the cross head.

The drawback to this instrument is that the cross head (due to the small distance between the sighting slot and the object slot) only gives an accurate line for short distances.

A set of boning rods is another good old-fashioned standby of the foreman; but how effective!

The rods (of which there should be a minimum number of three) must be well made for accurate work, the heads truly square with the body, and each rod exactly the same length as its neighbour to as fine a limit as possible.

The manner of their use is shown in Fig. 12. Two pegs are levelled in at convenient points, one rod is held by an assistant at the forward station and one by an assistant at the intermediate station while the man at the sighting bar looks along the top edge, indicating by hand signals how far the intermediate peg is to be driven to produce a level line. Sometimes it is found more convenient not to drive the peg in at the time of boning, but to pack up with bricks and pieces of slate and to come back afterwards and drive in the peg to the height required.

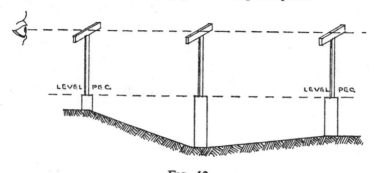

FIG. 12

Boning rods may be used directly to level in road kerbs, pavings, gradients, shallow drains and the actual levels of a small plot of ground. This last is rather laborious and not to be recommended but is a useful thing to know. It simply requires pegs to be driven in at, say, 10ft. centres each way, the tops of the pegs being boned in as shown in Fig. 13 when the distance from the top of each peg down to the actual ground level is taken as near as maybe with a two foot rule, thus giving a grid of reduced levels but with no connection to any existing bench mark.

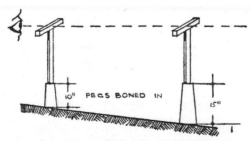

FIG. 13

C

This method, although somewhat rough and ready, is undoubtedly useful in obtaining the contents of bulk excavation in a quick manner so as not to hold up the employment of expensive excavating machinery or keeping a gang waiting.

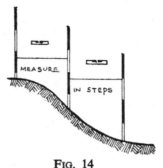

FIG. 14

One final point is worth bearing in mind. Plans are assumed to represent a perfectly horizontal plane and all measurements have to be read in strict accordance with this assumption. If, therefore, the actual ground is found to be steeply sloping, all lineal measurements must be stepped as shown in Fig. 14. To do this, set up two ranging rods, stretch the tape between them, level up and mark off the required distance perpendicularly.

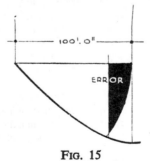

FIG. 15

Fig. 15 makes it clear what sort of error is likely to ensue from taking plan measurements and transferring them directly on to sloping ground without adjustment for slope. The horizontal measurement would fall short of the required dimension by the amount coloured black in the diagram.

A foreman who can set out without the aid of the clerk of works or the resident engineer, who can get the whole contract going independently, at once commands respect and confidence from his employers and from the engineers.

After all, the contractor is obliged by his contract to set out the works.

One cannot do better than quote the requirements of the "General Conditions of Contract, Forms of Tender, Agreement and Bond for Works of Civil Engineering Construction."

Clause No. 17 of this document states:

The contractor shall be responsible for the true and proper setting out of the works and for the correctness of the position levels dimensions and alignment of all parts of the works and for the provision of all necessary instruments appliances and labour in connection therewith. If at any time during the progress of the works any error shall appear or arise in the position levels dimensions or alignment of any part of the works the contractor on being required so to do by the engineer shall at his own expense rectify such error to the satisfaction of the engineer unless such error is based on incorrect data supplied in writing by the engineer or the engineer's representative, in which case the expense of rectifying the same shall be borne by the employer. The checking of any setting out of any line or level by the engineer or the engineer's representative shall not in any way relieve the contractor of his responsibility for the correctness thereof and the contractor shall carefully protect and preserve all bench-marks site-rails pegs and other things used in setting out the works.

It is clear from the above clause the great importance attached to setting out and the very serious financial effects on a contractor who should find himself in error (despite the supervision of the clerk of works or resident engineer) especially if the works had proceeded some way before the discovery of the error.

Chapter III

SETTING OUT ROADS AND SEWERS

DESPITE the title I shall reverse the order of the work and commence with sewers. In works which are wholly new, the layout of the roadways and footpaths undoubtedly comes first for the convenience of placing the lines of sewers and other services; but after the preliminary setting out of the work it is the sewers which occupy the immediate attention of the contractor, who should lay all hidden services before any further work is proceeded with.

Many large sewage contracts consist in laying a complete scheme through the roadways, streets and by-ways of an existing town, the City Fathers having decided to do away with earth closets, privies, and private septic tanks and cesspools, also as a consequence the objectionable night soil disposal squad.

In all undertakings of this nature some pretty problems are involved which tax to the full the skill of the engineer planning the work. A large scheme of closet conversions may involve not only the actual alterations from dry and earth closets to w.c.s encompassing hundreds of individual houses and terraces, but probably cinemas, hospitals, recreation grounds, and public buildings, each of which has its own private means of sewage disposal. In these cases the closets themselves do not require conversion since the w.c. pans and water-waste preventers are already existing; the problem is to make a smooth turnover from septic tank, cesspit or small private sewage disposal works to a public sewer.

These are the principal points which the engineer has to keep in mind when drafting his scheme, apart from the actual constructional problems of the lines of sewers and the lay-out of the sewage disposal works itself.

A competent engineer will of course resolve all these problems on the drawing board and in his specification and bills of quantities before even a sod is turned.

Then comes the contractor with his workmen and machinery

to put into practice what the engineer has theorised over: It will be found that there are many points of disagreement between what *seemed* possible to the engineer and what *is* possible on the field of operations. An experienced contractor (which suitably translated means *the foreman*) will be constantly alert for all such difficulties, always ready to compromise, always ready to do what is expedient without worrying the engineer about every small divergence from the plans and specifications, or assuming that the engineer is wrong, or that he had missed an important point. What may appear to the foreman as very important on the job (or at least on that particular portion of it) may be a triviality when compared with the whole scheme. Remember, the engineer has spent many months considering every eventuality long before the contract was let as a complete job.

Consider a sewage scheme such as has just been briefly described. It runs through an old town and extends for five miles until it reaches the proposed sewage disposal works with its attendant pump house, filter beds, storm water tanks, sludge lagoons, etc. The line of sewers will not of course be all in the one straight line (if it were so the task would be much easier) but will run through all the principal streets and roadways, doubling back on itself and going round blocks of houses, over bridges, underneath canals and finally, perhaps, crossing a river by means of an inverted syphon.

Do not fall into the prime error of starting at a point chosen at hazard and working up to each section on the principle that "sufficient unto the day is the evil thereof!"

Before undertaking any work spend a couple of days, plan in hand, walking round the job, considering, just considering. Ignore the black looks of the boss!

Plans of sewage schemes have certain peculiarities which make them differ considerably from the general run of building and civil engineering work.

There is first of all the main lay-out which is invariably to a scale of 1/2500th, generally being a tracing from an up-to-date ordnance map of the town, or at least so much of it as is involved in the scheme.

On this plan will be superimposed the line of the proposed sewer drawn in black, the manholes being indicated by circles generally tinted red. Should there be a separate system for the surface and storm water the scheme is often drawn out in green or blue ink, the manholes being tinted in the same colours.

To simplify the scheme, the sewers are divided up into various distinct lines, each designated by a letter, while the manholes receive a number; all manholes on any particular line go by the number preceded by its designatory letter: Thus on Line A there might be seven manholes which would be numbered A.1, A.2, A.3, and so on to the end of the line. Line F would commence F.1, F.2, etc. These letters are used throughout on all plans, in the specification and the bills of quantities.

It is not possible to convey much information on the 1/2500th plan beyond the course of the sewers. To overcome this difficulty a separate plan is made of each line of sewer (one for each designatory letter) showing the levels of the land and of the manhole inverts together with the gradients of all pipes.

FIG. 16

It is at this juncture that the tyro comes up against his first obstacle, not a very big one it is true, but a point which is somewhat confusing at first sight. Sewer sections are drawn out generally to a scale of 1/500th longitudinally, whilst the vertical scale is to a much larger unit, often 1/10th of an inch to one foot, so that we have the somewhat perplexing convention of two different scales being employed on one integral drawing: Thus a 6in. diameter sewer 41ft. 8in. in length and 10ft. deep would be drafted on a line one inch in length horizontally and one inch vertically as indicated in Fig. 16. Fig. 17 shows a section taken from an actual job, the horizontal scale being 1/500th, whilst the vertical scale is 10 feet to the inch, or one foot equals a scale of 1/120th.

Another peculiar thing about sewer sections is that manhole depths and sewer inverts are shown set off from a horizontal line (Datum) which changes in value from one part of the line to the next. Let us follow through from Fig. 17 starting with manhole

A.24 where the section commences, to manhole A.22 where the line ends. The base line at the commencement is figured 300ft. A.O.D. which means three hundred feet above ordnance datum whilst the self-same line a little further on is figured 270ft. A.O.D. How can one line represent two different levels with a rise or fall of thirty feet between them? It is simply a draughtsman's convention, a means to an end, and is dictated by the size of the drawing paper or drawing board available, or even the personal preference of the engineer.

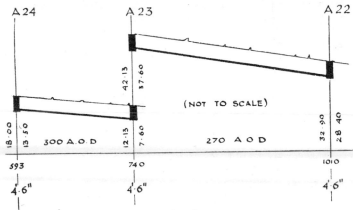

FIG. 17

This manner of working enables sections of drains on a steep incline to be conveniently placed on the paper without running right down the drawing from top to bottom, so wasting a lot of paper. It in no wise affects the physical characteristics of the work or its carrying out.

Reading manhole A.23 (the last manhole on the 300ft. datum) we note that the ground level is 12·13ft. above the line whilst the invert level is 7·60ft. The depth of the manhole to channel invert must therefore be as follows:—

Ground Level	..	..	12·13
Invert Level	..	..	7·60
Depth to Invert	..	..	4·53

Manhole A.23 is repeated from the 270ft. A.O.D. line when the check is as follows:—

Ground Level	..	..	42·13
Invert Level	..	..	37·60
Depth to Invert	..	..	4·53

The arithmetic of the procedure is exactly the same as a change point in levelling.

To ensure that the working is well understood, the operation should be followed through although in actual practice conditions this need not be carried out every time.

			ft.	in.
A.O.D. No. 1	..	..	300	0
A.O.D. No. 2	..	..	270	0
Difference ..	..	..	30	0

			ft.
Ground Level (a) ..	..		42·13
Ground Level (b) ..	..		12·13
Difference ..	..	..	30·00

			ft.
Invert Level (a) ..	..		37·60
Invert Level (b) ..	..		7·60
Difference ..	..	..	30·00

These three important cross checks should always be equal and this checking is one of the first things to be carried out. It is surprising how easily errors may occur through a slip-up of the draughtsman or the engineer in the actual process of draughting. Too often such discrepancies pass unnoticed until a harassed foreman finds two lines of drain trying to pass each other.

Another important thing to notice from the sample section is that manholes A.24, A.23 and A.22 are all 4ft. 6in. deep to channel invert, although the gradients vary. Gradients in fact are not related to depths, but only to falls or rises from one point to another. A sewer or drain may be set to a gradient of say 1 in 50 whilst the drain may be at any depth from one foot to 30 feet. Engineer's drawings have the gradients noted in between manholes, which helps to keep before the engineer the rate of slope at which he is working and, at the same time, is of great use to the contractor when setting out, thus saving a lot of rather fiddling calculations on the job; work which might otherwise be done on the back of a time sheet in the lee of a hut, with a blinding snowstorm raging, the head and shoulders of the mathematician being covered with a cement sack.

The correct setting of two manholes of course gives the gradient between them, but, as so often happens in practice, the manholes are spaced over 200ft. apart making the reading of the sight rail a chancy business in which case an intermediate sight rail is called for; unless the gradient is known it is impossible to set the intermediate rail at its correct height.

A line of sewer may be laid to pass underneath a high factory wall so that it would be impossible to see the sight rail on the opposite side. In an instance of this sort it would probably be convenient to paint a sight rail on the wall itself, the height to be calculated by simple proportion from the known gradient.

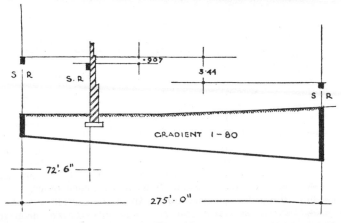

FIG. 18

Assuming a distance of 275ft. between manholes as in Fig. 18
with a factory wall intervening at a distance of 72ft. 6in. from
the first manhole. The given gradient is 1 in 80. From these
data we know that the sight rail of the distant manhole must be
set 3·44ft. below that of the first manhole, all of which may be
very easily done, when we come to a full stop! The distant sight
rail being blotted from view by the high wall.

The only way of overcoming this obstruction is to calculate
the gradient up to the wall, mark a line or datum at the correct
height on each side of the wall, and so lay the drain in two
portions with the knowledge that the gradients are exact.

The wall is 72ft. 6in. from the centre of the first manhole; the
gradient is 1 in 80. Obviously the sewer will have fallen by
nearly a foot by the time it reaches the wall; for every 80 feet
horizontally that there is in 72ft. 6in. the vertical measurement
declines by 12in.

$$\frac{72·50}{80·00} = ·907\text{ft.}$$

Mark a line on the wall 10¾in. (full) below the level of the first
manhole invert which should be sufficient to set the first stretch
of sewer to an accurate gradient.

The gradient on the far side of the wall is of course set out
afresh using a new series of sighting rails, which need not be
related as regards height above ground level to the first line of
sight rails; the gradient must of course remain unaltered.

An engineer's drawing not only indicates manholes, gradients,
depths, and diameter of sewer, but also gives distance of drain
between centres of manholes. All such measurements are running totals commencing at the top or shallowest manhole, this
latter being numbered zero, the last manhole on the line being
the full chainage for that particular series of manholes and line
of sewer.

Having decided on the line of sewer to commence, search for
the engineer's preliminary pegs or other setting out marks (perhaps an existing manhole) and set up ranging rods to mark the
beginning and end of the line, with as many intermediate poles
ranged in as may be found convenient.

Assuming a run of sewer 1,000ft. in length there may very well
be five or six manholes on such a run with distances between

them varying from 200 to 300 feet drawn out on several related but separate sheets. Muster all these sheets together from the bundle of contractors' drawings, lay the first sheet from which you are immediately working on your desk, and pin the remainder (in their correct order) on the walls of the hut. It is then possible to take everything in at a glance and in an orderly manner.

There will undoubtedly be many different gradients to work to in a line of sewer of this length necessitating several sets of sight rails.

The trenches will almost certainly be excavated by machinery. Set the uprights of the sight rails sufficiently wide apart to allow the excavator to run easily between them and to pass on without taking the whole lot with it.

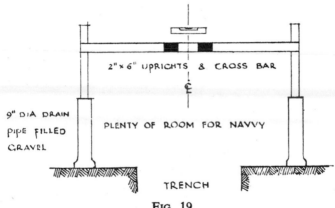

FIG. 19

The uprights should be out of sawn 2in. × 6in. (do not be cheese-paring about this) and should be planted truly vertical, setting them up in the time-honoured drain pipes filled with gravel. The cross bar must be levelled in expertly and may also be out of 2in. × 6in. finished with a target face painted on it; a broad white band finished on the external edges with black as shown in Fig. 19.

On this cross post or sighting rail the central line of the trench should be accurately marked. It will be found a great convenience (although a little more trouble) to fix a steel bracket on each upright (indicated in Fig. 20) into which the sighting rail slots, enabling the rail to be moved for the passage of the excavator.

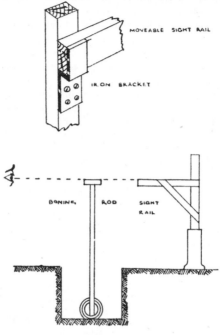

FIGS. 20, 21

Another form of sight rail is shaped like a gallows bracket and erected on one side of the trench only so as to allow the passage of the machine without disturbing the sighting rail, as in Fig. 21. In my opinion this is a slipshod method and not to be recommended for two main reasons. The first being that from the centre of the trench the foreman has to judge whether the T head of the traveller is level with the sighting rail *laterally* instead of longitudinally; secondly, he has to look transversely from the centre of the trench to the gallows bracket at the side of the trench as indicated in Fig. 22.

The function of the sighting rail is merely to give the gradient;

it has nothing to do with the depth of the manhole or sewer invert. It follows that it is immaterial at what height the sighting rails are erected. They should of course be set conveniently so that the foreman neither has to mount a ladder nor lie on his stomach, deer-stalking fashion, in order to obtain a clear line of vision.

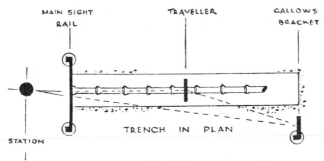

FIG. 22

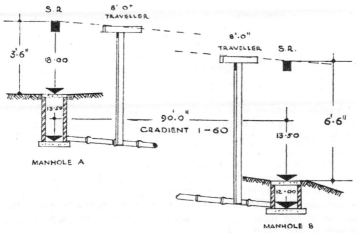

FIG. 23

The more usual method of erecting sight rails is to calculate the height from the length of the traveller or boning rod. Supposing it is decided to use an 8ft. traveller to set the gradient for the section of sewer shown in Fig. 23.

Manhole A

Ground Level (A.O.D.)	..	18·00
Invert Level ..	..	13·50
Depth to Invert ..	..	4·50
Length of Traveller	..	8·00
Depth of Invert ..	..	4·50
Height of Sight Rail	..	3·50

Manhole B

Ground Level (A.O.D.)	..	13·50
Invert Level ..	..	12·00
Depth to Invert ..	..	1·50
Length of Traveller	..	8·00
Depth to Invert ..	..	1·50
Height of Sight Rail	..	6·50

To check the above calculations the difference in the levels of the sight rails must equal the total given fall in the sewer.

Manhole A

Ground Level (A.O.D.)	..	18·00
Height of Sight Rail	..	3·50
		21·50

Manhole B

Ground Level (A.O.D.)	..	13·50
Height of Sight Rail	..	6·50
		20·00

Height of Sight Rail A	..	21·50
Height of Sight Rail B	..	20·00
Difference	.. .. ..	1·50

Invert Level A	.. ..	13·50
Invert Level B	.. ..	12·00
Difference	.. .. ..	1·50

There are several other methods for setting up sight rails but the one explained here is the best standby for all occasions.

The traveller itself should be constructed out of 2in. × 5in. with a well set cross head painted white with black borders to form a target. The foot of the traveller should be furnished with a bracket of half round iron about 2in. long, bent at right angles and screwed to the central leg in order that it may sit truly on the invert of the sewer pipe as indicated in Fig. 24.

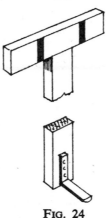

Fig. 24

It will probably be found that the 8ft. traveller will serve many sections of the line of sewer despite the numerous variations in gradient which occur on a contract of any size. An experienced foreman can pick out at a glance almost how many times he can re-use a boning rod. Where the pipes are laid in deeper trenches from say 15ft. onwards, it is obvious that a fresh length of traveller becomes necessary. It is good practice to paint in prominent numerals the length of the traveller on the rod itself, and also on each set of sight rails where that particular length applies.

When the nature of the work calls for an exceedingly deep trench, for depths at anything over 15ft., travellers become unwieldy. It is preferable in that case to make use of a gradient board shown in Fig. 25.

It may be constructed out of 2in. × 9in. to a recommended length of 12ft. with a stout handle at each end. The lower edge is cut and planed to the exact gradient indicated on the engineer's drawing whilst the top edge is square. The commencement of the trench is sunk to the exact depth and a brick or square of concrete laid in the bottom to mark accurately the invert level of the pipe. Trial pegs are then driven in at less than 12ft. intervals and the gradient board is laid on top and levelled up by means of a bricklayer's level. If the first 12ft. of trench is carefully done the rest of the trench will follow very easily. The principal difficulty of this method is working in a confined space combined with the frequent testing of the pegs. However, since such work generally applies to only a small part of the contract, it is not such a serious problem.

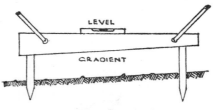

FIG. 25

Very deep sewers are always laid in headings or tunnels.

To set out a heading requires experience. The great difficulty in this class of work is that one is unable to judge in what direction the excavation is going, the whole of the work being underground, so that it is necessary to tunnel in a certain fixed relation to points on the surface and at the same time to judge in what direction you are going underground.

The obstacle to overcome springs from the fact of being unable to obtain a direct sight ahead, either with the theodolite or the level; the surveyor is obviously facing a blank wall of earth the whole time.

In sewer construction which commences in open cut and eventually runs into tunnel for say 250ft. to re-emerge into open cut once more, the direction of the excavation may be set out by the following method indicated in Fig. 26. The tunnel is commenced from the open trench, which at this point is of course dug wide

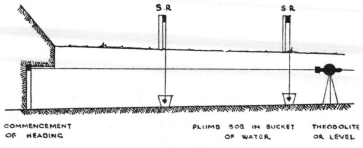

COMMENCEMENT
OF HEADING

PLUMB BOB IN BUCKET
OF WATER

THEODOLITE
OR LEVEL

FIG. 26

enough to permit of all operations and free movement so that the framing for the tunnel may be inserted as the work proceeds. The first six feet of the tunnel is then driven, the direction being judged as near as possible from the run of trench behind and from the directions of the sight rails already fixed over the open trench. This part of the work is only approximate to enable a start to be made, nevertheless it must be carried out with all possible accuracy. Having made an inroad of 6ft. into the heading, a cross head or support should be fixed (one of the temporary timbers will of course serve for this purpose) and the

D

central section should be painted to form a target as for the ordinary sight rails.

The level is now set up in a convenient portion of the open trench, the instrument is centralised by means of the plumb bob and a sight taken in such a way that the cross hairs of the diaphragm coincide exactly with the two plumb lines attached to the sight rail as shown in Fig. 26.

It is easy to understand that any third point which coincides exactly with two previously fixed points must be in a straight line with the latter.

A useful hint to prevent undue swaying of the plumb lines is to immerse the plummets in a bucket of water placed immediately underneath. The gentle resistance of the water will stabilise the circular motion of the weights without displacing the plumb line from the vertical.

The chief objection to carrying the work out with a level is that the telescope cannot be rotated on its vertical axis, requiring that all sights must first of all be taken on to a cross rail placed at a convenient height for the instrument, fixed and marked, eventually being transferred by means of a plumb line to the cross head of the tunnel timbers, giving further opportunity for errors, apart from the extra time involved. The use of a theodolite then is always to be recommended, a shot being very easily marked either to the roof of the heading or to the base; in fact both shots may be made as a test of the true vertical position and the accuracy of the instrument.

As the work proceeds further and further into the tunnel, an assistant with a flash lamp must illuminate the target each time it becomes necessary to take a sight.

The theodolite or level may be altered in position from time to time. The instrument can be set up inside the tunnel and a sight taken back on to the two original plumb lines first erected. A reversal or transit of the telescope should automatically put you in a straight line with the original setting.

During the whole operation of driving the heading and keeping the right direction levels and gradients must be carefully watched. It is a good plan to set a concrete post to an exact datum at the open end of the tunnel, leaving the rough excavation at least 6in. proud of all gradients set off from the datum peg, finishing by shovel to levels set off from the peg by means of straight edge and bricklayer's level. Never be afraid to spend a little time on spadework; it is much cheaper than having to fill in excess excavation with concrete.

It is now time to leave the sewers and to concentrate on the sewage disposal works.

A modern sewage disposal works consists of a series of tanks which receive the crude sewage direct from the sewers and pass it on from tank to tank, each one of which is controlled by a network of weirs, overflows, penstocks and valves, so that finally the solid matter has been screened, settled and deposited in various compartments according to its physical and chemical state, leaving the effluent to be passed (by means of a rotating filter arm) through a graded filter medium consisting of various sizes of granite or clean clinker. The effluent (which chemists assure us is harmless) is finally disposed of by means of an outfall pipe discharging into the nearest river.

The solid portion of the sewage remaining is dealt with in various ways, being allowed primary and secondary settlements until eventually the dry residue is used for various classes of manures.

To enable all this intricate handling to be carried out a pump house is necessary which in reality is an ejector. Essentially it takes the form of an enclosed chamber which receives the sewage at a low level and, by means of compressed air, automatically let into the chamber (this is put into operation by the level of the sewage itself), lifts the complete contents to the required level in the tanks. In most cases it is found that a single pump house at the works is insufficient; an intermediate pump house, perhaps a mile away, has to be erected, the action here being different from that of the ejector at the works. The sewage at the intermediate station is received in a crude form and, by means of powerful booster pumps, is forced up what is virtually a rising main to the works.

Needless to say the levels between the intermediate station and the main station inverts are all important. To ensure accuracy seek out the nearest ordnance datum to each pump house. Set a level peg to the data given on the plans and concrete in. Then make an extended level using each peg as a back sight when the staff should show the same result whether calculated from the ordnance datum or the first two pegs.

The tanks themselves are simple in shape and construction, the only circular work being the filter beds which may easily be trammelled from a centre peg by means of an offset from a base line.

It is sufficient to say that the various tanks used for the reception of sewage are nearly always rectilinear and constructed in mass or reinforced concrete. For the most part they are set deep in the ground, the walls being battered for the sake of economy. The principal instruments required are the setting out line and square, supplemented by the plumb bob and dumpy level.

Having effectually disposed of the sewers, the roads and footpaths may now be taken in hand.

All roads are best set out from a line of centre pegs, the width between kerbs being set out equidistant each side of the pegs. The setting out pegs should be about 3in. square and 4ft. long so that they stand out well above the proposed finished surface of the roadway.

The main levels should be set off from a permanent datum peg concreted in and set about 3ft. above the kerb or crown. Set it well back from the scene of operations so that it need not be moved by reason of the roadways or buildings.

The setting out should be related to a base line and offsets all of which should be indicated on the drawings. This important direction is sometimes omitted from plans in which case a commencement should be deferred until the engineer supplies full data. Should any of the roads be set off at an angle the latter should be stated on the plans and set off from a base line, alternatively two offsets may be given, one at the commencement and one at the end of the road so that a line may be sighted between the two. Sufficient information must be given for any road to enable two ranging rods to be set up in order to give the true direction of the centre line.

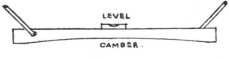

FIG. 27

One last thing; a camber board shown in Fig. 27. This board

might well be made in two pieces in the case of wide roads and screwed together on the job. It should be made out of 3in. stuff with two stout iron handles for ease of manipulation.

When the bottoming of the road has progressed so far, set up the camber board and construct a width of finished surface to the exact contour as shown by the placing of the camber board. A width of 2ft. is adequate, then repeat the process about 50ft. along, the finished surfaces so formed being used as guide strips. The road should be laid to a perfect contour. The foreman's friend, the boning rod, will once more prove of inestimable value in laying channels and kerbs, all of which should be boned in from the main datum peg set up at the beginning of the job.

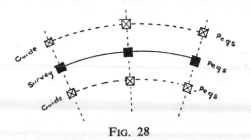

FIG. 28

Despite all precautions it is sometimes found necessary to move important pegs temporarily. Before doing so, set guide pegs each side of the main peg as shown in Fig. 28. It is then a simple matter to replace the peg in its original position merely by centring the peg with a steel tape. This is especially useful in the case of curve ranging where otherwise the replacement of a moved peg might entail a lot of repeated instrument work.

Chapter IV

SETTING OUT SIMPLE CURVES

A WELL-DESIGNED crescent is more than half the battle in the lay-out of a housing scheme; it is, in fact, a "selling point". A gentle curve to join up two main roads converging at right angles or at an angle larger than 90 deg., is a much better solution than joining by a straight line. An open-air swimming pool with one wall to a slow curve is a much more enticing place than a plain rectangle of glimmering water.

Then come the more utilitarian instances, where a factory boundary wall follows the curve of a siding, or a long slow curved embankment neighbouring on existing property, or even a loading bay and platform in reinforced concrete. All these instances require the ability to set out curves of more than a hundred foot radius without the aid of a trammel or centre peg, to set out arcs of a circle with intermediate obstacles in the way, or to set out curves when it is only possible to plot the beginning and end of the curve on the site. The work on the plan looks easy enough. It is when one comes to set it out 2,500 times larger on the actual job that the difficulties commence. The inexperienced try to surmount this fence by drawing the required curve to a much larger scale (say, a ⅛in. to 1ft., if it is a very large circle) and setting up offsets from a base line or from a chord, which, when accurately scaled, should give the required points on the circumference of the circle. *It never does!*

The contractor (blissfully unaware of the terrible ordeal he is in for) comes on to the site and commences to set his pegs according to the scaled dimensions, when to his horror the curve is anything but a curve, there are continual adjustments and lining-in by eye, efforts to range a series of radii from a central peg, and in the end an ungainly bulge or straight run in the smooth line of the curve, just where it counts the most. The reasons for the failure are that the principles of the method are entirely wrong. It is one thing to draw a series of curves and ordinates on the drawing board or a line of chords to a given circumference or to work from a given base line to a known curve. It is an entirely different matter to lay down a base line in the field (possibly several acres in extent) full size and project ordinates to the circumference of the circle *which isn't there!*

There is yet another and even greater error in the procedure, however.

The whole basis of setting out large curves and circles correctly is that of angular measurement.

Once the conception of angular measurement in the construction of curves is grasped (although at first glance the two things may appear to be far removed from each other) the going is straightforward and easy. The apparently simple facts that the angles contained in any triangle together add up to 180 deg. and that the angles contained in any quadrilinear figure together equal 360 deg. have a very important bearing on the setting out of circles.

Before commencing the main problem a few preliminary considerations will ease the path considerably and prevent us from getting bogged in a morass of mathematical and trigonometrical formulæ. There is nothing more confusing and destructive of clear thought than the endeavour to use mathematical formulæ "as you go along". Have a clear notion from the commencement of the exact significance of the terms and formula in use and most problems are half solved by this alone.

The tangent is an important property of a circle to start with, defined for our purpose as a straight line just touching the circumference of a circle and at right angles to the radius at that point. Three tangents are shown in Fig. 29.

| FIG. 29 | FIG. 30 | FIG. 31 |

The importance of this definition is to note that the angle formed between the tangent and its radius is 90 deg., an angle easy to set out. If we like to draw the quadrant of a circle and fill in numerous radii with their respective tangents as in Fig. 30 we find that we have almost drawn the circumference by straight lines alone combined with the comparatively simple process of setting out angles of 90 deg.; in fact, if we drew the radii extremely close together and followed it up by drawing in all the tangents we should have a perfect quadrant or circle as the case may be.

A knowledge of the tangent is useful but it has another function far more valuable.

Draw the quadrant of a circle once more and inscribe therein an angle of 45 deg. then draw the tangent, using the base as radius as shown in Fig. 31.

The tangent (marked "T" in the diagram) always bears a strict proportion to the length of the base. It is easy to see in the example chosen that the base and the tangent equal each other. The proportion is, therefore, 1: 1 or $1/1 = 1.00$.

As a second example, draw an angle of 60 deg. and it will be found that the proportion of the tangent to the base is almost $1\frac{3}{4}$ or 1.750.

Construct an angle of 30 deg. and it will be found that the tangent is almost $.600$ of the base line.

To find the proportion of the tangent to the base of the triangle it is not necessary to construct a diagram each time; fortunately, it has already been done very accurately for us.

A table of natural tangents will be found in any book of mathematical tables. The exact value of any tangent may be ascertained with as much ease as looking up a sum of pounds, shillings and pence in a ready reckoner (which is all that a set of mathematical tables is).

In leaving the definition of the tangent it must be noted that it is a straight line lying immediately outside, but just touching the circumference of a circle at a point.

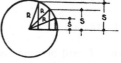

FIG. 32

The next important property of a circle is the sine indicated in Fig. 32. The sine lies *within* the circumference of a circle and is the proportion which the vertical lines bear to the radius. The sine of 30 deg. is $\frac{1}{2}$, or $.50$. The sine of 90 deg. is 1.00.

Like the tangents, all these values may be obtained direct from a book of tables.

The radius in each instance is treated as a unit of 1·00. In the case of the tangent, the base is treated as 1·00, while with sine it is the hypotenuse which is unity or 1·00.

There are other very useful properties of angles and circles which, however, need not trouble us here. Once having mastered the measuring of tangents and sines, we are well equipped to set out simple curves. Should any other formulæ be needed, they can be picked up en route.

Now for the practical work. A theodolite reading to 1 min. is preferable, but if one is not to hand a good level with a horizontal circle reading to 2 min. will do, providing that the site is fairly level. A theodolite may be tilted, enabling the telescope to sight a pole in practically any position, whereas the tilt obtainable on a level is practically nil. There is nothing more maddening than to find that the head of the staff or rod is just below the range of vision due to the extreme slope of the ground. To guard against this latter contingency (in the case of a level) a few 12ft. rods should be taken along as well as several 8ft. rods for general ranging purposes.

A bundle of good, stout pegs not less than 2ft. long by 2in. by 2in., a 100ft. steel tape, a heavy hammer and a set of arrows complete the equipment.

The example chosen as shown in Fig. 33 is that of a boundary wall enclosing a factory. The wall is intended to be construtced in 14in. brickwork with 18in.-wide buttresses at 12ft. centres. It joins up two straight runs of walling and is 6ft. high above ground.

The plan is drawn to a scale of 1/2500th. For setting out purposes it gives the radius of the curve and the chord, 950ft. and 850ft. respectively.

As a setting out plan it is rather meagre, but is well up to the standard of such plans and, with the knowledge we are about to acquire, is ample for the job.

There are also some reduced levels noted, which are a great help. It will be noted at once that there is roughly a drop of 8ft. between the base of the wall and the centre for setting out. Check it exactly as follows: level at end of curve, 213·01; level at centre peg, 204·63; the difference amounts to 8·38.

If we are confined to the use of a level only, we shall obviously

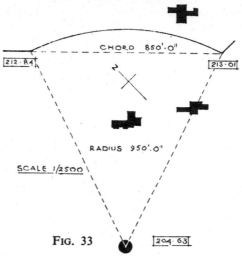

CHORD 850'.0"

212.84

213.01

RADIUS 950'.0"

SCALE 1/2500

Fig. 33   204.63

require 12ft. ranging rods, which will just enable the top of the pole to be seen. The next thing to note is that the radius of the circle is 950ft., while the chord is 850ft. It is very important here to remember that while the radius is a fixed measurement chosen by the engineer or architect, the chord should be checked on site between the two pegs marking the beginning and end of curve. Should there be any difference between the actual measurement and that shown on plan, the site dimension should, of course, be worked to (at the same time notifying the clerk of works).

It is necessary to know the angle subtended at the centre before we can commence the actual setting out of the curve.

The sine gives us this in a most wonderful way. As shown in Fig. 34, halve the chord and drop a line at right-angles, which will, of course, go straight to the centre of the circle. We now see that the sine of the angle is merely the proportion which the measurement of

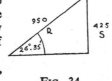

Fig. 34

$\dfrac{850}{2}$ is to 950. Stated more simply $\dfrac{425}{950}$, which reduced to a decimal fraction = ·4471.

Twice the angle equals the required angle subtended at the centre. The table of sines gives an angle of 26 deg. 35 min. corresponding to the result ·4471. Twice the angle there amounts to 53 deg. 10 min.

As an informative check, set this out to a scale of 1/500th, using an ordinary celluloid protractor, and you will find that it can be easily read by eye alone to 53 deg.

We have already gone a good way to setting out our curve. We have obtained or had given to us from the setting out plan the following facts, which can now be tabulated: 1, length of chord from beginning to end of curve 850ft.; 2, radius of curve 950ft.; 3, included angle found by calculation from sine tables 53 deg. 10 min.

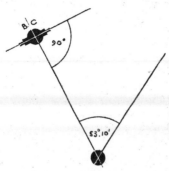

Fig. 35

Having these important details before us, setting out the actual curve will be comparatively easy. The remaining process is more or less a repeat action. Master the first step and the following steps are mere repeats of the first. Plant a ranging pole at the centre of the circle, walk to the beginning of curve and set up the theodolite or level immediately over this peg as indicated in Fig. 35.

Civil engineers and surveyors set out a simple curve by means of deflection angles combined with a series of chords each exactly 100ft. in length. The method is simplicity itself.

One man remains at the instrument, swings the telescope to the required deflection angle, while the chain men simply step off the 100ft. measurements successively at a given signal from the surveyor standing at the theodolite.

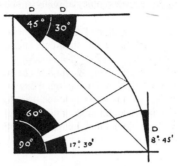

FIG. 36

The meaning of deflection angle is clearly explained in Fig. 36. Draw the quadrant of a circle and its full chord, then the tangent.

The deflection angle (marked D) is the angular measurement in degrees between the tangent and the chord; 45 deg. in the diagram, which is half the value of the angle subtended at the centre of the quadrant.

Select an angle of 60 deg. at the centre and draw the chord. The deflection angle this time is 30 deg. from the tangent; and so it goes on. If the central angle were 17 deg. 30 min. the deflection angle would be 8 deg. 45 min.; if the central angle were 2 deg. the deflection angle would read 1 deg. The importance of all this is that the deflection angle always equals half the value of the angle at the centre of the circle.

An engineer when setting out curves speaks of "degree of curve", and he always has in mind a chord of 100ft.

Fig. 37 shows that the smaller the degree of curve the flatter the curve and the larger the radius, but for general building purposes it will not be necessary to make use of this method of working.

It follows that before a deflection angle can be set out it is necessary to have a tangent line from which to set it.

Let us go back to our theodolite left standing ready set up over the peg at the beginning of curve (B.C.).

Swing the telescope round until the ranging rod at the centre of the circle is sighted, turn back a full 90 deg., signal to the chain man to put in another pole, and there is your tangent.

FIG. 37

It will be very useful to range the tangent from the end of curve (E.C.), but on looking at the setting out plan we see that it is an impossibility; there are buildings in the line of sight each way.

Such a difficulty (often met with in practice) is easily over-come by using our knowledge of sines and tangents.

The exact length to the apex of each tangent can be rapidly calculated by means of the tables.

Fig. 38 shows what is required.

Tan. 26 deg. 35 min. $= \dfrac{T}{950}$ therefore $\cdot 5007$

$= \dfrac{T}{950}$ and $\cdot 5007 \times 950 = T = 475.67$ft.

It only remains for us to measure 475ft. 8¼in. full from B.C., set up a pole, and we have the apex of the tangent.

If now we could put in a peg in the centre point of the curve we should have a useful intermediate check before starting to set out the pegs.

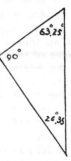

FIG. 38

It will be noted from the plan that it is impossible to sight through from the apex to the centre of the circle because, unfortunately, a building is again in the way. It is possible, however, to sight from the centre of the chord (425ft.) to the apex, giving a straight line to measure along.

It will be necessary to find the central ordinate (marked X X in the diagram) by trigonometrical calculation, after which we can easily set up the centre point of the curve.

Fig. 39 shows us what we have to do.

It is simply the distance X X deducted from the radius of 950ft., leaving as remainder the distance X O, the ordinate required.

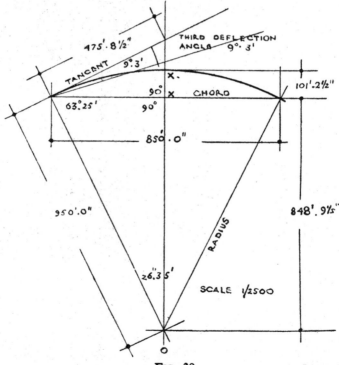

Fig. 39

Once more the table of tangents is used.

$$O \: X = \text{base of triangle} \: \frac{425}{B} \: \text{therefore} \: \cdot 5007 = \frac{425}{B} \: \text{and B}$$

$= \dfrac{425}{\cdot 5007}$ which is 848·81ft. $\quad$ X X = 950ft. − 848·81ft. $\quad$ Say, 101ft. 2¼in.

We have now established a very important checking station, namely, the central point of the curve, and also the correct distance from the curve, giving us the degree of curvature (not to be confused with the engineer's "degree of curve" already described).

Back once more to the beginning of curve (B.C.), where all we have to do is to set out a series of angles deflected from the tangent line as shown in Fig. 40, adding them in succession until we reach the end of curve (E.C.).

FIG. 40

We already know that the deflection angle is equal to half the value of the angle subtended at the centre. The deflection angle is designated D.

To find the value of D refer to the sine tables.

$$\text{Sine} \: \frac{D}{2} = \frac{50}{950} = \cdot 0527, \: \text{which is 3 deg. 1}$$

min., also equals $\dfrac{D}{2}$ and so D will be equal to 6 deg. 2 min.

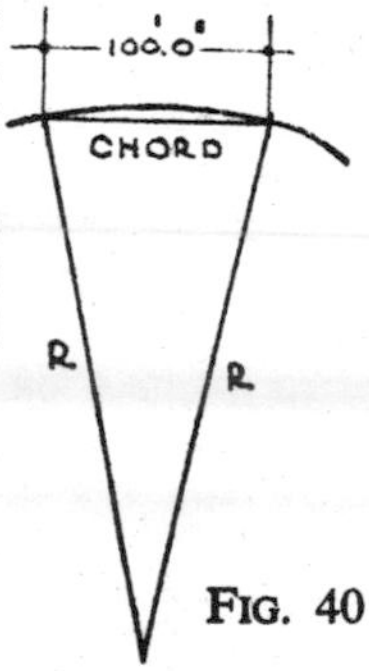

For our first deflection angle we sight to the apex, set off an angle of 3 deg. 1 min. and chain a 100ft. For the second deflection angle we set off 6 deg. 2 min. and chain 100ft. from the last peg; for the third deflection angle set off 9 deg. 3 min. and again chain a 100ft., and so on until the curve is complete.

The eighth deflection angle will bring you roughly to within 52ft. of the end peg, so that there will be no need to continue, but as a final check the curve may be extended past the end peg for another full deflection angle.

You will note the simplicity of the procedure. The small amount of computation is of course done in the drawing office or foreman's hut, and then it is merely a question of repeating the same deflection angle each time, setting off from the tangent line and chaining successive measurements each of 100ft.

A hint in actual practice is to use the sights of the theodolite or level for aligning the chain men, only using the telescope as a final check for each shot.

Never let discarded setting out or survey pegs remain in place or you may find that you have taken an important sight on to one of these pegs with disastrous results to your curve.

There is one other very useful method for setting out curves by means of deflection angles and a table of chords.

With this method the chord of 100ft. is dispensed with as also the set deflection angle.

Whatever the radius and included angle may be, the deflection angle may be set off at random, say, 4 deg. 30 min., double this, making 9 deg., look up the corresponding chord in the tables, multiply by the length of the radius and chain off the length so found from beginning of the curve.

Each chord is calculated thus and chained off from beginning of curve (which is, of course, the centre of the instrument) for as many chords as you may find convenient to put in.

As a check on the method let us go back to Fig. 39 and test the main chord which we know to be 850ft. The deflection angle is 26 deg. 35 min., the centre angle is 53 deg. 10 min., the radius given is 950ft., and the chord from tables will be ·8945. Chord multiplied by radius (·8945 × 950·00) equals 849·775. There is a discrepancy here of nearly 3in. in 850ft. This is not due to inaccuracy of working or setting out, but to the fact that the tables of chords are computed to two minutes, while the sines and tangents are computed to single minutes and not seconds. Had the tables been calculated to a finer degree of accuracy it would probably have been found that the central angle was 53 deg. 9 min. 30 sec.

The exact reading to within 10 sec. could of course have been ascertained by the theodolite, but the nature of the work does not warrant the extra trouble.

To line in a curve as large as the example to within 3in. of chord and centre ordinate would be quite permissible in actual practice, any such small discrepancy of course being trued up by secondary measurements and adjustments.

It is easy to see why a table of chords is so useful in setting out a curve. It is simply the table of natural sines set out in a different manner.

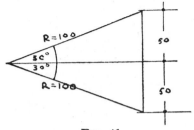

FIG. 41

It is twice times the sine of half the included angle as shown in Fig. 41.

Sine 30 deg. is $\dfrac{50}{100}$ = ·50, which from table of chords is 60 deg. = 1·00.

When setting out curves (or, for that matter, any setting out) take plenty of time over each step; read each angle twice and from both the verniers. There should of course be 180 deg. difference between the two readings. If you find that one of your circumference pegs is undoubtedly out of line, start afresh; check the tangent very carefully and all previous deflection angles.

It will be seen from the diagram that it is unnecessary to be able to sight to the centre of the circle before ranging the tangent.

This operation can easily be done from beginning or end of curve or from the apex, or even setting up a triangle from the centre of chord, but sighting to the central angle is always preferable if it can be carried out.

Always rely on actual site meaurements and sight lines whereever possible in preference to computation.

There is one other useful method for setting out curves of large radius where the centre is inaccessible. It is very useful to know but troublesome to accomplish.

In Fig. 42 we have a curve of which the chord is 1,000ft., the length of the central offset is 150ft., and this comprises all the information we have. The central angle and the radius are not given, and no clear line of vision is obtainable on the job, except by working solely from the main chord.

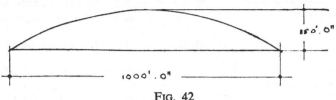

FIG. 42

With the use of a table of chords the difficulty is easily surmounted.

The first thing to consider is that a table of chords is of no use unless we know the radius of the circle in question.

The radius is easily calculated as follows: 1. Find the deflection angle. 2. Twice the deflection angle = central angle of half chord. 3. Sine of central angle of half chord gives radius.

The above three directions can now be translated into the actual figures affecting our example.

1. $\dfrac{150}{500}$ = tangent of deflection angle = ·300 = 16 deg. 42 min.

2. Central angle of short chord = 2 × 16 deg. 42 min. = 33 deg. 24 min.

3. Sine of central angle = radius (R) ÷ 500, i.e., ·5505 = $\dfrac{500}{R}$ and R = $\dfrac{500}{·5505}$ = 908·80ft. or 908ft. 9¼in.

The remainder is simple. Set up the theodolite over the central point in the curve, set off as many convenient deflection angles as you wish, multiply each of the latter by 2 and look up the resulting angle and chord from the tables, and multiply the printed fraction by 908·80. Repeat the whole process for the remaining half of the curve.

As a simple test, the radius multiplied by the chord for the full central angle should equal 1000·00.

The full central angle is equal to twice the central angle subtended by the small chord as follows:

2 × 33 deg. 24 min. = 66 deg. 48 min.

This angle is really slightly too large by about two minutes and is due to our using tables which are not calculated to seconds.

Chord for angle 66 deg. 48 min. = 1·1010. Radius × chord = 908·800 × 1·1010 = 1000·589ft. Calculated for an angle of 66 deg. 46 min. = 1·1005 × 908·80 = 1000·13ft.

There are many other extremely useful means for setting out curves and circles entailing the use of tables and formulæ, but these would only lead to unnecessary complications in the simple work we have in hand.

The whole of the work can be satisfactorily set out with the use of the few simple tables and formulæ given, namely, tangents and sines. A table of chords, while very useful, is only a table of sines in another form and may be dispensed with.

Chapter V

THE DUMPY LEVEL

BEFORE actually describing the dumpy level it might be interesting to note that there are four main types of level in use by surveyors and contractors: the water level, the Y level, the dumpy level and the quickset or precise level, although the first two types mentioned are practically superseded.

The water level is a very useful, ingenious and straightforward instrument to use. It is automatic, requiring no levelling or adjustment, although this is made possible on the instrument by use of convenient setscrews. No matter where, or how, the level is set up, it gives a true level sight immediately.

It consists of a horizontal tube (which need not be set horizontal) with a piece of glass tubing set vertically in each end; the whole apparatus is filled with coloured water which, of course, rises to an exact level in each glass tube whatever the setting of the instrument might be. The surveyor then merely sights along th top of the coloured water to obtain his levels. This instrument has no lenses and is on this account very restricted in use but, nevertheless, of the greatest help on building work.

The Y level is practically the same as the dumpy level, but differs in the following respects: The telescope is held in a Y-shaped clamp at the eye-piece and object end, and may be rotated a full 360 deg. by the fingers so that the spirit bubble, instead of being on top of the telescope, is suspended underneath, whence the mean difference of two readings automatically corrects an instrumental error. The telescope may also be unclamped from the Y brackets and replaced end to end, again correcting any error in the setting of the bubble with regard to the line of collimation.

As to the basic adjustments required when using all the levels mentioned (with the exception of the water level), they are the same in principle, although the manufacture of the precise level makes the accurate setting up by means of footscrews unnecessary.

The dumpy level consists of a telescope with a spirit level mounted on top; the horizontal axis of the spirit level being set exactly parallel to the line of collimation of the telescope, in such a way that when the bubble of the level is in the centre of its run, a person looking through the telescope is peering straight ahead in a perfectly horizontal plane. Over long distances refraction modifies this statement considerably but need not be taken into account here. The curvature of the earth also plays a very important part, affecting the apparent levels between two points a long distance apart, making the difference larger than it really is. The discrepancy in turn is offset to some extent by the incidence of refraction already referred to. How it comes about may be seen from a glance at Fig. 43, which is very diagrammatic indeed, and bears very little relationship to actuality.

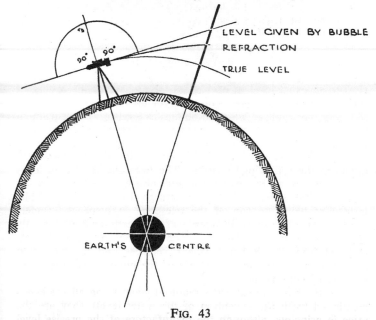

FIG. 43

Before these natural effects are worth the surveyor's serious attention, the extent of the range over which the levels are taken must be immense, and for all practical purposes they can be neglected on building and general engineering works.

But to return to the dumpy level. The instrument is set on a solid base and levelled up by means of three footscrews very accurately machined with closely-cut threads and large milled heads for easy manipulation by the thumb and forefinger of each hand. These screws (when slowly revolved) push upwards against an underplate, thus raising or lowering the telescope and bubble as the case may be.

The chief parts of the dumpy level are designated in the following table and shown in Fig. 44.

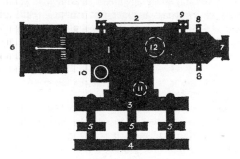

FIG. 44

1, telescope; 2, spirit level; 3, base; 4, underplate; 5, footscrews; 6, object lens covered by ray shade; 7, eye glass; 8, capstanheaded screws for level; 10, slow motion screw; 11, clamp, 12, focusing screw.

The telescope reverses the image so that the base of the staff appears upside down whilst the right hand appears as the left hand. This peculiar view of things (so much in keeping with most of to-day's thought) causes considerable confusion at the first encounter, but one soon becomes accustomed to reading the staff upside down.

There are levels in which an extra lens is inserted to bring the image the right way up, but (I am told) clarity of reading is lost and the extra expense involved does not warrant the addition of an added lens in an instrument of this nature.

Another method employed is to use a staff with the numbers

already inverted so that a normal image is obtained of the graduations, but here again the foot of the staff still appears upside down, making the result more confusing to my mind than the direct reading with the inverting lens.

It is not often appreciated what an important and useful adjunct to the level the ray shade is. It is a cap or cylindrical cover with a sliding hinged lid made to cover the object glass completely and securely when not in use, the whole thing being easily slid on to the end of the telescope.

In certain lights, particularly if the day is cloudy with the sun half breaking through, and where it is necessary to obtain a sight against a dark background of trees or hedges, great difficulty will be found in focusing a clear-cut image. Pull out the ray shade so that it forms a hood over the object glass, shielding it from the brightly diffused rays of the sun, when all haziness will disappear. The ray shade can be used in the same manner on an extremely bright and cloudless day. On these occasions, to look through the telescope is a great strain on the eyes unless the ray shade is used to its fullest extent.

Another very neat use for the ray shade is to take rough gradients or falls in ground. It will be noted that there is a sighting slit in the shield with a corresponding arrow on the body of the telescope, whilst the shield itself is graduated either in degrees or to set gradients. Its method of use is as follows:

The instrument is levelled up, the ray shield pulled out to its fullest extent so that the sighting slit is clear, and a reading taken on the staff of a sloping field, say, a reading of 7·45. The assistant then moves the staff to the highest point of the sloping ground and in a straight line with the instrument as indicated by hand-signals from the surveyor, who now takes another sight, looking through the sighting slot, at the same time revolving the ray shield until he again finds the reading of 7·45 on the staff. The number of degrees, or the gradient through which the ray shield has revolved, is then easily read off against the arrow on the body of the telescope.

The clamp screw must always be left free before turning the telescope; this is the first thing to look for. When the staff is sighted approximately, screw down the clamp screw and bring to final adjustment by means of the slow motion screw.

Some instruments are provided with sighting vanes which may

be seen over the top of the telescope, and thus the staff may be brought into view approximately before it is actually focused. This device is a great relief to the eyes; at least, I have found it so.

It will be found that having focused the staff perfectly with a good, clear-cut image, it is impossible to take a reading because the cross hairs are indistinct or are not even visible. Turn the eye piece slowly and the cross hairs will stand out black and sharp without in any way disturbing the focussing of the staff.

The bubble itself will be dealt with later on, but it can usefully be mentioned here that most modern instruments have a mirror fixed over the bubble in such a manner that the surveyor can see the disposition of the level without moving himself from the eye piece. When the level is not in use, the mirror (which is encased in gunmetal) clamps down on top of the bubble tube as a protection.

On some instruments there is a small circular bubble which plays about in its little box and is a great help in the preliminary setting up of the level, enabling a practised surveyor to save much wear and tear in the footscrews. Such small plate bubbles are, however, more frequently attached to the quickset or precise level.

Now we can proceed with the actual use of the dumpy level. There are three main adjustments necessary to know for the correct usage of the dumpy level:

(a) Setting up and bringing the bubble to the centre of its run. This action should be performed once only for each series of levels. In the case of the precise level the bubble is centred for each shot by means of the micrometer screw situated at the eye piece end of the telescope.

(b) Setting the longitudinal axis of the bubble parallel to the line of collimation. This action is common to all levels and is most important.

(c) Setting the cross hairs or diaphragm central with the exact centre of the object glass.

Adjustment (a) is carried out by placing the telescope parallel with any two footscrews as shown in Fig. 45; bring the bubble half-way correct, turning the telescope through 180 deg. and bringing the bubble exactly central.

Use the footscrews gently the whole while to obtain this result. When the bubble appears to be truly set, swing the telescope round at right angles and repeat the process, using screw 1 as indicated in Fig. 45. Now gently revolve the telescope through 360 degrees noting if there is any displacement of the bubble, slightly adjusting all three footscrews as necessary, after which the bubble should remain stable in whatever position the telescope is placed.

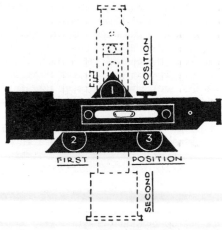

FIG. 45

Now for adjustment (b). It does not follow that the level is reading correctly because the bubble is in the centre of its run. The spirit level may be correctly centred while the telescope is on the slope as suggested in Fig. 46. If the discrepancy is small (as

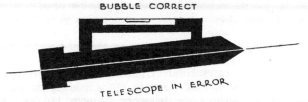

FIG. 46

it generally is) it is most difficult to detect and all sorts of inexplicable errors creep into the work. One visual indication that the axis of the bubble and that of the telescope are not parallel is in carrying out adjustment (a). If, despite the most meticulous setting, the bubble persistently runs out of setting on a small turning of the telescope you may depend on it that the spirit level itself needs adjusting, but by how much?

Refer to Fig. 47 where the telescope is shown set up out of level, the diagram showing the effect very much exaggerated.

Drive in two pegs 200ft. apart and a central peg. Take care to ensure absolute accuracy with these measurements and use a steel tape.

Set up the level over the central peg. Mark diagonals on the peg, and use a plumb bob so that the centre of the instrument is vertically over the intersection of the diagonals. Some levels are already provided with a centre hook for using a plummet. Level up by means of the footscrews as accurately as possible (ignoring the suspected error in the instrument itself) and take the reading on each peg, say 6·82 for peg No. 1 and 7·14 for peg No. 2.

From Fig. 51 we know that this must be correct irrespective of any error in the instrument; the central placing of the level on a fixed vertical axis ensuring that the levels *are relatively correct*.

Now refer once more to Fig. 47 where it will be seen that the level is this time set up beyond the two pegs. Set out the distance to the centre of the peg as before, namely 100ft., bring the bubble as perfect as possible by means of the footscrews and again read the levels on to the two pegs. It must be obvious that if the level is in true adjustment the difference in levels between points 1 and 2 taken from point 3 will be ·32ft. in height: 7·14 − 6·82 = ·32.

Assume that the reading this time on peg No. 1 is 4·93 while peg No. 2 reads 5·75, the difference in levels is ·82ft., so that there must be an error in the instrument.

Fig. 47 shows how the error may be corrected. It is merely one of proportion.

The pegs are inserted at intervals of 200ft. and 100ft. respectively. It follows that the error of ·50ft. must represent two-thirds of the distance down the staff as shown in Fig. 47. To make the longitudinal axis of the bubble conform with the line of collimation it is only necessary to focus the telescope carefully on to the staff at the correct height (by calculation) and finally to bring the bubble to the centre of its run by manipulating the capstan headed screws (Mark 9) as indicated in Fig. 44.

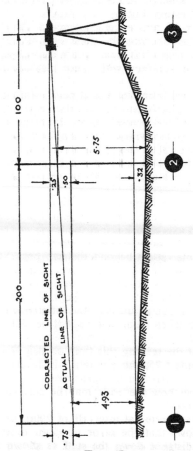

FIG. 47

As already mentioned the required computation is one of simple proportion.

Level on Peg No. 2	..	..	..	5·75
Level on Peg No. 1	..	..	..	4·93
Difference	..	..	..	·82
Difference (second reading)	..	..	·82
Difference (first reading)	..	..	·32
Error	..	..	..	..	·50

·50ft. represents from the diagram two-thirds of the height required to bring the instrument truly level so that the following calculation gives the required figure to add to the staff reading at Peg No. 2.

·50 2/3 Error.				
·25 1/3 „				
Staff reading Peg No. 2 ..	..	..	5·75
Computed error ..	..	..	..	·25
				6·00
Staff reading on Peg No. 1	..	..	4·93
Computed error ..	..	..	..	·75
				5·68

Difference in levels

Corrected level on Peg No. 2 ..	..	6·00
Corrected level on Peg No. 1 ..	..	5·68
Difference in levels	..	..	·32

The above calculation is sufficient proof to set the level correctly. Once the level is set, and the capstan headed screws tightened, it should not require adjusting for a very long time. In making this test be sure that the pegs are spaced at equal distances as the whole operation is strictly one of proportion. The longer the distance between the pegs the greater the degree of accuracy in the result.

The third adjustment (c) is also very important. An object

when viewed against the diaphragm should appear clear cut and fixed, immovable. If the readings on the staff appear to jump up and down or to move with each movement of the surveyor's head, it indicates that the diaphragm is not centred exactly with the alignment of the centre of the object glass. A simple movement of the capstan headed screws (Mark 8) Fig. 44 will eventually put this right by trial and error.

These two principal adjustments take some time to accomplish, but once they are made the instrument may be used with absolute confidence; should things appear wrong after this you know that it must lie either with your own reading of the staff or error in computation.

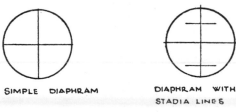

SIMPLE DIAPHRAM   DIAPHRAM WITH
                      STADIA LINES

FIGS. 48, 49

Two of the more usual types of diaphragm are indicated in Figs. 48 and 49. The one being simple cross hairs (natural spider's web skilfully stretched across a thin metal frame) and the other lines engraved on a thin sheet of glass, the two shorter lines, known as stadia lines, being used to measure distance from the centre of the instrument without actually using a tape. The inclusion of stadia lines leads to errors in reading; it is only too easy to mistake the lines especially if the light is poor. For setting out or taking levels stadia lines are unnecessary.

When setting up the dumpy level make certain that the bubble is truly central and remains so when slowly revolved through 360 degrees. It is to be noted that the instrument must be revolved slowly (to whizz the telescope round is very misleading) and no adjustment whatsoever either of the footscrews or the capstan headed screw of the bubble should be made once readings have commenced; if it should be found that such adjustments are necessary, then the setting up of the level is faulty, all readings must be cancelled, and the whole process of setting up must be gone through afresh.

The basic rule for levelling is never take a reading until the bubble is central.

No matter how short the distance of the sight or how relatively unimportant certain levels may appear to be, always adhere to the rule so that it becomes an automatic habit to look to the position of the bubble before noting a reading.

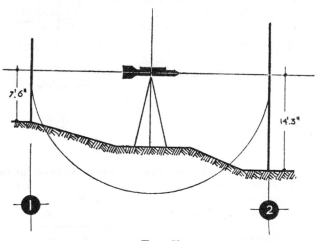

FIG. 50

In Fig. 50 it is necessary to know the difference in levels between points 1 and 2. The dumpy level is set up midway between the two points and readings taken on the staff when it is found that the height of the staff at point 1 is 7ft. 6in. while that at point 2 is 14ft. 3in. The required answer is:—

Level at point No. 2	..	..	14ft. 3in.
Level at point No. 2	..	..	7ft. 6in.
Difference	..	..	6ft. 9in.

Now take the same two points again as indicated in Fig. 51 but this time do not trouble to level up except roughly so that the bubble is playing up and down the tube as the telescope is revolved.

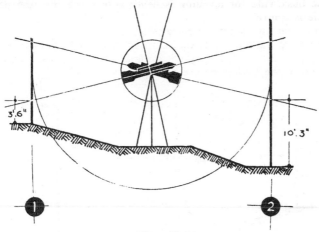

Fig. 51

Provided the level is stationed exactly central between the two points the difference in levels will be accurately ascertained.

Level at point No. 2	..	..	10ft. 3in.
Level at point No. 1	..	..	3ft. 6in.
Difference	..	..	6ft. 9in.

It is especially to be noted here that if the line of collimation were used in relation to other levels at various points of the survey, the result would be hopelessly in error, but since it is only a question of the difference in levels between points 1 and 2 the answer is correct; always providing that the instrument is placed centrally.

This result seems to refute, or rather take away, some of the importance attributed to the basic rule of centralising the bubble; in fact many practised surveyors often take levels in this manner. While this is useful knowledge to have it is far safer for the foreman or agent to trust solely to the correct setting up of the instrument. There are so many situations in day-to-day practice where it is impossible to obtain a central station for the dumpy.

If we now glance at Fig. 52 where the level is shown set up beyond points 1 and 2 with the bubble out of centre the error in reading is at once apparent.

Level at point No. 2	12ft.
Level at point No. 1	2ft. 9in.
Difference	9ft. 3in.
Supposed difference in level ..	9ft. 3in.
Actual difference in level ..	6ft. 9in.
Error	2ft. 6in.

Despite the fact that the placing of the level with the bubble out of centre as shown in Fig. 52 would give a false result, a true reading could still be obtained without re-setting the level, by the following method.

It will be noticed that the bubble tube is graduated either in tenths of an inch or in two millimetre divisions. Each division represents anything from one minute to 20 seconds of arc according to the sensitivity of the instrument. A constant is supplied with each instrument and either noted in the lid of the case, or engraved on the bubble itself.

For ease of calculation we will take a bubble where each division represents one minute.

Fig. 53 shows the method to be followed in reading from the bubble. This manoeuvre (which is purely mathematical) is not one to be recommended for general use, but is very useful to know in the case where a succession of levels has to be taken and perhaps pegs driven in and set to various heights, when the surveyor glances down at his instrument only to remember that he has forgotten to bring the bubble central.

A simple calculation here will save a lot of duplicated effort, especially if the sights are over a short distance. Should the sights be long distances, say 750ft. or over, there is only one course to be adopted; re-set the instrument and start afresh, not forgetting to throw out all pegs already set on the line.

Suppose Fig. 53 represents an extreme sight of 80ft. from the

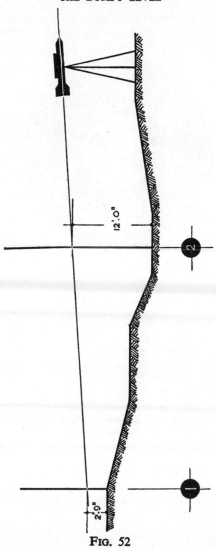

Fig. 52

centre of the instrument to the point on the ground where the level peg is to be set, the following working results.

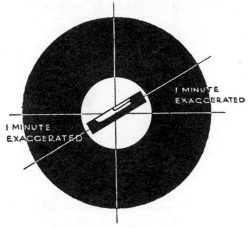

Fig. 53

Distance from centre of instru-
ment to peg ..   ..   .. =   80ft.
Radius of circle (Fig. 53)   .. =   80ft.
Diameter of circle   ..   .. = 160ft.
Circumference of circle   .. = 502·65ft.

If the bubble tube were rotated vertically through 360 degrees as shown in Fig. 53 it would describe a circle of which the circumference was 502·65ft.

If the bubble tube were rotated through an angle of only one minute (as indicated in a greatly exaggerated form in Fig. 53) the amount of deflection or elevation would be 1/360th of the circumference for one degree further divided into 60 parts for one minute.

The full error in reading the bubble in the position shown in Fig. 53 is obtained as follows, not forgetting that feet must be reduced to inches, and that degrees must be reduced to minutes.

$$\frac{502·65 \times 12}{360·00 \times 60} = \frac{6031·80}{21600·00} = ·28\text{in.}$$

The working shows that the maximum error at 80ft. distance corresponding to one graduation on the bubble equals ¼in. full, therefore any intermediate points on the same line of levels would be correspondingly less and could be neglected. It is now a comparatively easy matter to make the necessary adjustments on the levels previously taken. In some cases a ¼in. would be of no importance; in others, steelwork and engine beds in particular, it would be of sufficient importance to warrant an all round alteration in the given levels.

In the manufacturers' specifications of theodolites and levels the sensitivity of the bubble is always quoted in so many minutes or seconds of ARC, this being the most useful information. It applies to any sight (within the limits of the particular instrument) that the surveyor may be called on to take. Thus, if the greatest distance at which ·01 of a foot may be read is 750ft. the surveyor is enabled to work out beforehand the maximum possible error in his workings for one or any number of graduations on the spirit level, and can work to those limits.

With the latest type of precise or quick-set level the graduation of the bubble tube is unnecessary, since the instrument is set level before each reading is taken, as has already been described, while the micrometer screw is engraved for reading degrees or gradients.

Whereas the true dumpy level is manufactured solid with the base, the line of collimation being set at right angles to the vertical axis of the instrument, the precise level ignores this principle, the line of collimation being pivoted about the vertical axis.

The term "collimation" when applied to a level or theodolite means the line of sight passing through the exact centre of the eye glass and the object lens, the cross hairs coinciding with both the lenses.

With the level goes the Sopwith staff, together with its several variations; for all practical purposes the only staff used in England for general survey and building work.

There are three customary lengths in use, 14ft., 16ft., and 18ft., while for cramped positions a 6ft. and 9ft. staff may be obtained.

The 16ft. and 18ft. staffs are not to be recommended for ordinary use due to the difficulty of holding such a long length truly vertical. It is always preferable, if possible, to obtain steep changes in levels by turning points, that is, shifting the instrument and reading back on to the last position from a more convenient standpoint.

All staffs are telescopic, each section being slightly less in width than the lower section. When extended, the various sections are secured by a strong brass spring with a lip on it preventing the extended portion from sliding back.

When the staff is being used to its full extent it is most important to make certain that the spring and lip are in their correct position, otherwise the graduations on the extended portion will not register the correct distance from the foot of the staff. It is surprisingly easy to fall into this trap.

The staff holder must be instructed to hold it truly vertical, so that the line of sight through the telescope strikes the face of the staff at right angles. Where certain readings are of great importance, admitting of no error, it is usual for the staff man to wave the staff slowly backwards and forwards in an arc, the surveyor meanwhile taking several readings, the least reading, of course, being the one required.

The Sopwith staff is divided into whole feet and tenths of a foot, making each main division of a foot equal to 1·20in. These latter divisions are in turn divided into tenths so that each of the small gradations is equal to ·12in. or 3/25th of an inch which for all practical purposes is always reckoned as a bare ⅛in.

It is possible with a first class level and a well defined staff to read ⅛in. at 1,200ft., and by inspection to read to 1/16in. at 500ft.

A typical Sopwith staff graduation is shown in Fig. 54, together with some specimen readings.

Do not start in straight away and expect to read the reversed image through the telescope. This method of attack will only bring confusion and disappointment.

Accustom yourself to reading the staff first of all the correct way up without the use of the telescope, and, although the following remarks might appear obvious, note them one by one.

(a) Whole feet are figured in red. (Shown hatched in Fig. 54.)

(b) Tenths of a foot are numbered in black alternate divisions only in order to avoid a confusing network of figures on the face of the staff when viewed at a distance through the small aperture of the telescope.

(c) Hundredths of a foot are not figured, but indicated by graduations in black and white. This is a most important observation. Reading of the white spaces through the telescope causes great confusion to the beginner. Each space is of equal importance; they all have to be played on like the keys of a piano.

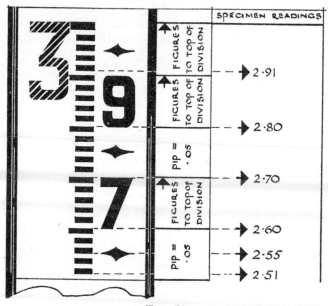

Fig. 54

To help in reading the smaller graduations each ·05ft. is indicated by a black pip, which you will notice comes level with the top of a white division.

The pip denotes the top of a white division and not the bottom of a black division.

All figures, whether they be the large red ones for the whole feet or the small black numbers for the sub-divisions are printed to coincide with the top of a graduation, as indicated in Fig. 54. The pip is a most useful landmark when you are lost in the reading; merely count the divisions backwards or forwards from it and you have a simple subtraction or addition to ·05ft.

There is one important convention for use with the Sopwith staff; the arabic numeral for five is substituted by the Roman V. This method of numbering is resorted to in order to avoid confusing 5 and 3 for long distance sights.

In practice it is often found that the surveyor cannot read the nearest foot due to the limited field of vision on the object glass. To obviate this the staff has a small figure in red (not shown in Fig. 54) printed on the same side of the staff as the main figures which indicates the number of feet preceding.

Fig. 54, which only shows a small portion of a staff reading up to 3·00ft. would have a small 2 in red printed at ·60 and ·30ft. respectively to tell the surveyor that he is now sighting between 2·00ft. and 3·00ft. His telescope might be concentrated somewhere about 2·65ft., neither the large red figure 3 or 2 being within vision.

As a preliminary course of instruction, try placing the staff against a wall and reading all the red figures, then reverse the staff reading the same figure again. The effect is strange. Repeat the process with the sub-divisions (both tenths and hundredths) and very soon reading the reversed staff will present no more difficulty than with the staff in its correct position.

The ABC of staff reading may be summed up as follows: (a) Look for the nearest red figure; (b) note the nearest black figure; (c) the pip means ·05ft.; (d) each new foot commences with a *whole space*.

Chapter VI

LEVELLING AND THE LEVEL BOOK

IT IS safe to say that no building work can be undertaken without making use of levels, even if it is only laying a simple house floor or a garage washing space to be laid to falls; when it comes to large undertakings, bridges, canals, railway cuttings, sewers, tunnels, or reservoirs, a mastery of levelling is *sine qua non*.

We are accustomed to speak in a loose way of levels, heights, and depths (all of which are really interchangeable terms) without being entirely aware of the meaning of our words.

For instance, one might say, "Build that buttress 4ft. 6in. high so that it comes level with the brick wall," and we should be quite content to regard this as a full and adequate instruction enabling us to carry out the work and fulfil the intentions of the person who gave the order.

It is only possible to carry out an order in these terms because we are already on the job, and can see exactly what is required, our minds and common sense supplying a mass of data not given and unexpressed in speech. Had these instructions been given to a person who had not previously seen the job, he would be quite unable to carry out the work for lack of data.

Let us consider once more these simple instructions to construct a wall buttress and see what is missing.

The order states that the buttress is to be built to a height of 4ft. 6in., in which case it will finish level with the top of an existing wall.

If the builder had no previous knowledge of the site he would require to know three main points as suggested in Fig. 55.

(a) Is the existing wall 4ft. 6in. from ground level?
(b) Is the existing wall a retaining wall 30ft. high from ground level on the open side with a dimension of 4ft. 6in. down from the top on the other side?
(c) Is the existing wall built in a cutting 4ft. 6in. deep?

NOTE: The dimension of 30ft. is merely taken as a case in point.

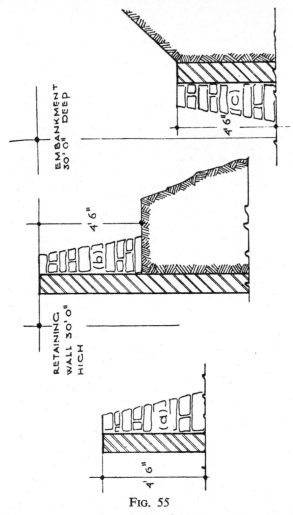

EMBANKMENT 30' 0" DEEP

4' 6" (a)

4' 6"

(b)

RETAINING WALL 30' 0" HIGH

(c)

4' 6"

Fig. 55

If the required work is as example (a) the construction is straightforward, but if as in example (b) or (c) it would entail ascending a bank 25ft. 6in. high or lowering materials down to a level of 30ft. from normal working level before the footings could be laid. In practice, of course, all this information is shown on a plan and section, all questions are answered neatly by reading the plans and notes thereon; nevertheless, the whole process of thought just described has been gone through before the plans could be drawn and the various levels and dimensions calculated.

It is all a question of levels, that is, a point from which to start, a mark of some sort from which to reckon heights and depths. To do this successfully everyone must obviously start from the same point.

The Government wisely decided to name the point from which all levels in the British Isles should be calculated. They chose the mean sea level at Liverpool, but later on altered this to Newlyn near Penzance. In consulting ordnance maps one frequently comes across both sets of levels or bench marks as they are called (not on the same map, of course). This has no effect on the working conditions providing that one is clear as to which datum is being worked to, since all levels are *relative to some fixed point*.

The mean sea level is, of course, a midpoint between high and low water, which element, being what it is, should provide us with a completely level line around the rugged coasts of Great Britain, which is surprisingly good reasoning for our Government, seeing that there are no steps in the sea.

The mean sea level is thus the datum from which all other levels in the British Isles are calculated as indicated in Fig. 56.

The chief symbol for indicating this series of ordnance bench marks is a broad arrow supporting a flat base as shown in Fig. 57.

This mark is cut and incised on rocks, buildings, gate posts or other features which are not likely to shift or sink. The staff is held level with the centre line of the horizontal base of the bench mark as shown in Fig. 57. At main trigonometrical stations the bench mark consists of a slotted plate in gunmetal or bronze into which a little table can be fitted to form a secure bed or bench for the placing of the foot of the staff as shown in Fig. 58, hence the name bench mark.

The series of levels shown on a plan are generally related to ordnance bench marks, since the block plans required by urban and rural district councils for the passing of plans are invariably drawn from the ordnance survey maps, on which are recorded bench marks at suitable intervals An intermediate type of level is also given on ordnance survey maps, known as spot levels, giving actual ground levels at the particular spots marked, say,

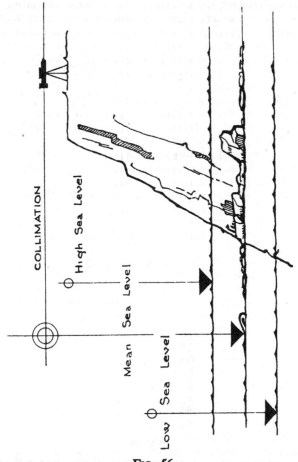

FIG. 56

in the centre of a roadway or a canal path. These levels are only correct at the time they are taken, and may vary considerably afterwards by reason of new road surfacings, lowering or raising of roadways, or new works of any nature. The use of spot levels from ordnance maps should not be relied on for accurate work, but nevertheless are very useful for giving one a rough idea of the job, especially where a preliminary scheme is required to be undertaken with reference to some distant site.

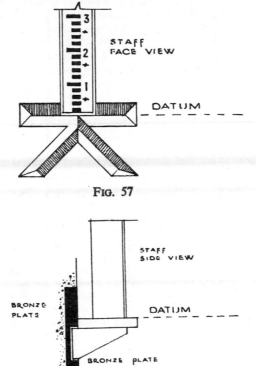

Fig. 57

Fig. 58

Sewage and water schemes call for particular care in the choice of levels and their setting out: An undertaking in one part of the country generally has to link with a similar installation in another area. It is very important, therefore, that the datum shall be the same for both schemes.

There are two main methods for recording levels.

(a) By collimation (height of instrument).

(b) By rise and fall.

It is a matter of preference for the individual surveyor as to which method shall be used, a question of what you have been accustomed to. Neither of the systems can claim advantage over the other. All levels should be recorded methodically in a surveyor's level book specially printed for the purpose, a very useful series of these books (printed for either system) being about 7½in. by 4¼in., containing about 80 leaves bound in stiff linen with an elastic band attached; such a book fits very conveniently into the pocket.

One method I have personally found to be very successful for recording levels is the following.

Draw out as shown in Fig. 59 a level book ruling on a piece of tracing paper about 9in. by 12in. and run off a dozen or so sun prints from this, stretch the sheets on to separate pieces of cardboard and keep one sheet for each job. The record sheets can thus be filed with each job, and in addition the stiff cardboard backing is very useful on the actual work; no matter how windy and boisterous the day, all flapping and tearing of sheets is avoided. Follow out the full routine always, even for one level. Record it in the book with heading, date, description and name of surveyor.

To set the level up hurriedly, jot the reading down on the back of a time sheet and wait until you get back to the office is all too easy, and as likely as not a waste of time. When you wish to make use of the information (possibly due to a sudden telephone call from the architect or engineer), you frantically search in your pockets for the envelope on which you have jotted down the important level, having completely forgotten that you wrote it on a time sheet which you threw away the day before yesterday, or alternatively you manage to fish it out of your pocket, but wonder what on earth it means.

System is essential above all in taking and recording levels. In using the collimation method what we are really doing is to note the height of the horizontal axis of the telescope above sea level, and proceed to make all the calculations from this datum by dropping imaginary perpendiculars from the line of collimation down to the various level pegs as shown in Fig. 60.

TITLE OF JOB   DATE

Back Sight	Inter	Fore Sight	Collim	Reduced Level	Distance	Remarks
4·93			214·93	210·00	·00	On B.M. 210·00 Gate
	5·93			209·00	25·00	
	7·82			207·11	75·00	
	6·84			208·09	125·00	
		6·43		208·50	150·00	End on Peg No. 5
		4·93				
5·93			214·43	208·50		On Peg No. 5
				210·00		
		1·50		1·50		Check

TITLE OF JOB   DATE

Back Sight	Inter	Fore Sight	Rise	Fall	Reduced Level	Distance	Remarks
4·93					210·00	·00	On B.M. 210·00 Gate
	5·93			1·00	209·00	25·00	
	7·82			1·89	207·11	75·00	
	6·84		·98		208·09	125·00	
		6·43	·41		208·50	150·00	End on Peg No. 5
5·93			1·39	2·89	208·50		On Peg No. 5
		4·93		1·39	210·00		
		1·50		1·50	1·50		Check

FIG. 59

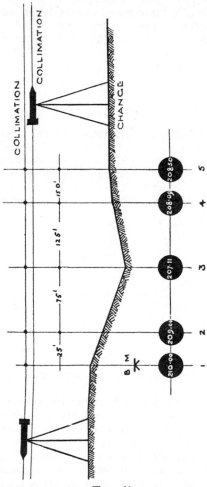

FIG. 60

The dumpy level is set up at some convenient spot, the staff is placed on the bench mark (210·00ft. in our example), and a reading taken, say 4·93ft., which measurement is to the exact centre of the telescope. We now have an invisible line stretched from the centre of the eyepiece to a point on the staff 4·93ft. above the bench mark, which mark is 210·00 ft. above mean sea level.

Bench mark	..	..	..	210·00ft.
Staff reading	..	..	..	4·93ft.
Height of instrument above mean sea level ..	..	..	..	214·93ft.

In the collimation method the rise and fall of the ground is not recorded, in fact the whole operation from start to finish is one of fall only in relation to the horizontal axis of the telescope; it is obvious that sights cannot be taken above this or the level would be tilted in an upward direction.

Referring once more to Fig. 59, we can proceed to Level Peg No. 2.

Collimation	..	..	..	214·93ft.
Staff reading	..	..	..	5·93ft.
Reduced level	..	..	..	209·00ft.

Level Peg No. 3

Collimation	..	..	..	214·93ft.
Staff reading	..	..	..	7·82ft.
				207·11ft.

Repeat the above process for any number of points, even for fore sights.

Now let us assume that still further levels have to be taken, but that the instrument is so placed that to continue is impossible unless the level is shifted to some more convenient position as indicated in Fig. 60. The shifting of the instrument for the continuation of levelling is known as a *change* or *turning point*. It is the frequent cause of mistakes for the beginner.

Consider peg No. 5 on which the first line of levels ends. The reduced level is, we already know by actual observation, 208·50ft. The new height to centre of instrument we do not yet know.

Place the staff on peg No. 5, read off the height, 5·93ft., and add to the last reduced level of 208·50ft., giving a fresh collima-

tion of 214·43ft., which in turn bears a true relationship to the
first collimation of 214·93ft.

Until familiarity and confidence in the use of change points
is obtained, always book the change in the level book as shown
in Fig. 59. This form of booking gives a much clearer idea that
a new range of levels has commenced and also that a different
collimation is being made use of.

A practised surveyor does not trouble to do this. He carries
on from the fore sight, inserting the new back sight and collimation level all in the same line.

A first glance at the back sights shows a difference of 12in.
between them, yet the line of collimation shows a difference of
6in. only; this appears to be an error until a detailed examination
is carried out.

Collimation level No. 1	214·93ft.
Collimation level No. 2	214·43ft.
Difference	·50ft.
Back sight No. 2	5·93ft.
Back sight No. 1	4·93ft.
Difference	1·00ft.
Reduced level peg No. 1 ..	210·00ft.
Reduced level peg No. 5 (F.S.) ..	208·50ft.
Difference	1·50ft.

The explanation of the discrepancy is now clear.

Point No. 5 (which becomes the new back sight) is 18in. below
point No. 1, while the instrument itself is set higher from the new
back sight by 12in., making a difference of 6in.

It is not necessary to use the last or fore sight as a change
point; any level peg could be used. For instance, you might
sight back to peg No. 3, of which the reduced level is 207·11ft.,
while the back sight might have been, say, 3·98ft.

Would this still give a correct result? It should do!

Reduce level peg No. 3 ..	..	207·11ft.
Back sight	..	3·98ft.
Collimation level	..	211·09ft.
Collimation No. 1 ..	..	214·93ft.
Collimation No. 3 ..	..	211·09ft.
Difference	..	3·84ft.

It is demonstrated that the instrument is now reading 3·84ft. lower than the first setting.

It follows that if all levels, both inter and fore sights, were reduced by 3·84ft., the results should be exactly the same.

Peg No. 1 back sight ..	..	4·93ft.
Difference in collimation ..	..	3·84ft.
		1·09ft.
Collimation level No. 3 ..	..	211·09ft.
Difference	..	1·09ft.
Reduced level point No. 1	..	210·00ft.
Peg No. 2 inter sight ..	..	5·93ft.
Difference in collimation ..	..	3·84ft.
		2·09ft.
Collimation No. 3	..	211·09ft.
		2·09ft.
Reduced level point No. 2	..	209·00ft.
Peg No. 3 inter sight ..	..	7·82ft.
Difference in collimation ..	..	3·84ft.
		3·98ft.

G

Collimation O,3   ..   ..   ..   211·09ft.
                                          3·98ft.
                                       _____

Reduced level point No. 3   ..   207·11ft.
                                       _____

The above method of working has been taken far enough to show that the theory is correct since all results equal the first levels taken.

Before dealing with the method of checking the results in the book it will be useful to describe another method for reading and booking levels by *rise and fall*.

This method differs from the collimation method by reason of the fact that each new level taken is used as a datum line for the succeeding reading as the following example. Back sight 4·82ft., intermediate sight 5·03ft., which shows a fall of ·21ft., and it is this reading which is entered in the fall column as shown in Fig. 59. The results by both methods must be equal as can be easily seen from an inspection of the two tables of readings.

To check the results for wrong calculations or booking errors proceed as follows.

COLLIMATION METHOD

The difference between the sum of the back and fore sights equals the difference between the first and last reduced levels.

RISE AND FALL METHOD

The difference between the sum of the rises and falls equals difference between sum of back sights and fore sights equals difference between first and last reduced levels.

The rise and fall method is slightly more complicated, but an extra arithmetical check on the working is obtained and is well worth while in the case of an extensive set of levels. It is to be remarked that it is only an arithmetical check and in no way guarantees against a mistaken reading due to taking a stadia line for a cross hair, for instance, or a transposing of figures or actual errors in the staff, or to the staff not being properly extended.

As an example of the mischances which might happen in a survey, take the back sight (Fig. 59) of 4·93, which might have been read correctly, but noted in the book as 4·39ft., or it might have been read as 4·83ft. and written down as such. None of these and similar errors could be discerned by a system of cross checking. On the other hand, had the back sight been erroneously written down in the level book as 9·43ft., the surveyor's preliminary knowledge of the site, the lie of the land or gradient, would give him a long pause before accepting this level. If a series of levels of fairly even run suddenly show a drop of 6ft. or 10ft., the surveyor computing from the book is entitled to ask himself the reason for the sudden difference; is it to be accounted for by an isolated ditch or bank? in which case it might not be a representative level; has a change of station been effected without a change point being recorded, or is it just a case of sunstroke?

At first sight the method of checking might appear somewhat mysterious; the reason why the difference between the sums of the back and fore sights should equal the difference between the last and first levels seeming to be particularly obscure.

By adding up the back sights and the fore sights we are really making one long staff of each, and upon comparing the length of one long staff with the other the difference must obviously equal that of the reduced levels, which are, it must be remembered, the same staffs under a different name.

Exactly the same reasoning applies to the rise and fall method, the difference here being obtained after deducting what is common to both.

As an example take the first two intermediate sights in Fig. 59.

Fall	1·00ft.
	1·89ft.
	2·89ft.
Rise	Nil
	2·89ft.
Peg No. 1 reduced level	210·00ft.
Fall	2·89ft.
Reduced level peg No. 3	207·11ft.

Follow through and analyse the series of levels given in Fig. 59, commencing and finishing at any point you choose, and it will be found that the results are correct.

In taking levels by means of the rise and fall method it is useful to bear in mind that an increase in the depth of the staff reading means a fall, while a decrease indicates a rise and always with reference to the preceding level.

Chapter VII

THE THEODOLITE

THE theodolite might be called the king of surveying instruments or perhaps it would be better to say the darling. It has a fascination for surveyors and engineers that few other intruments possess; its attraction never seems to wane from the moment of its acquisition in the full enthusiasm of commencing a career right to the days of retirement.

When old, full of experience and some disillusionment, your surveyor still cannot leave it alone, but must needs set the instrument up in his own garden and indulge in amateur astronomy, or the calibrating and setting of sundials; anything in fact so long as he has an excuse to fuss round and handle this wonderful instrument, the theodolite.

These splendid looking pieces of apparatus with their sleek telescopes, silver or glass circles, spirit levels, multiplicity of milled headed screws, magnifying glasses and Vernier gauges, are in reality astronomical telescopes in miniature, their principal use being the reading of terrestrial physical phenomena, of altitude and zenith angles, azimuth angles and bearings.

The astronomical telescope—a vast instrument weighing some tons, with special electrical machinery to move it—is furnished with a large horizontal and vertical circle for the reading of angles. The circles of these instruments might be anything from 10 to 20ft. in diameter, enabling fractions of a second to be read with astounding accuracy. Distances are so vast in astronomical calculations that the slightest divergence at the centre of the telescope axis means thousands of miles, or perhaps hundreds of thousands of miles, on the distant planet. But it is time we came down to earth, literally!

The complex and huge instruments of the astronomer cannot be carried round the countryside and set up for a field survey; hence we have the modern form of the theodolite in which some of the azimuth circles are as small as 3½in. diameter and yet may be read with accuracy to 20 or even 5 seconds: a splendid tribute to the skill of the instrument makers, which in turn calls for a complimentary skill on the part of the user. Beautiful instruments are turned out by Cooke, Troughton & Simms, Ltd., W. F. Stanley & Co., Ltd., Hilger & Watts, Ltd., and also Carl Zeiss.

Skill in the setting up and use of the theodolite is not a thing which can be "picked up". A casual talk on the building site or an occasional squint through the telescope will get you nowhere.

What is necessary, what is indispensable is hard and long application in the use of the instrument itself, and a thorough knowledge of the elements of Euclidian geometry and elementary trigonometry.

Let us not forget the object of our studies, which is to set out building works and not to make surveys. Working on this basis it is possible to limit the scope of the studies considerably, and yet to become a skilful exponent of the theodolite in the comparatively small field of work in which you will be called on to operate.

The theodolite is essentially a telescope set up on two circular horizontal plates, each of which may revolve full circle and independently of the other, the telescope being mounted by means of side supports (called "A Frames" from their shape) to the top plate or circle on which is engraved the Vernier markings.

Unlike the dumpy level, the telescope of the theodolite is free to rotate vertically through 360 deg or, to make a complete transit as a surveyor would say, the telescope tube being carried in the A frames by means of trunnions.

In making a complete revolution of 360 deg. the telescope revolves against a circle marked in degrees, whilst a double arm on the instrument, pointing in complete accordance with the telescope tube, indicates the angle through which the telescope has passed by means of a Vernier graduation.

In some instruments the circles revolve whilst the Vernier arm is fixed horizontally. The readings for any angle must, of course, be the same whatever method is used. It is a matter of individual choice.

The whole instrument is mounted on two parallel plates with three foot screws for levelling purposes, similar to the dumpy level, although the preliminary method of setting up the theodolite is somewhat different as will be described later.

From the centre of the base plate a plummet is suspended on a hook which, in some instruments, may be moved laterally in each direction for ease of centring, the movement allowed being about ¼in. either way, which movement is so skilfully managed that it may be achieved without disturbing the preliminary levelling up of the base.

A detailed description of the theodolite shown in diagrammatic form in Fig. 61 is as follows: The instrument depicted is assumed to be a Vernier reading to 20″ (seconds) without centring attachment and with rotating vertical circle.

A useful hint before the actual start. Place the mahogany case gently down on some level surface, open the lid carefully and note the exact manner of packing, with special regard to the placing of the object and eye lenses, and the manner of folding up the magnifiers: this simple little precaution will save much strain and, perhaps, damage to the instrument and the case, not to mention ruffled tempers.

Set up the tripod with the legs well spread and with *both* hands firmly supporting the body of the instrument, screw it on to the head of the tripod, and adjust as near as possible over the centre of the peg marking the commencement of the setting out or survey. Attach the plummet, wait for it to stop oscillating (instruct an assistant to cup it with the hands if necessary) and level up the base of the instrument as near as you can by eye alone. Look once more to the plummet and keep edging the instrument bodily including the tripod until you obtain an exact centring of the plummet. This operation (without a centring device) always takes a little time, but should not be hurried or scamped; it is the most important part of the whole business.

Before screwing the theodolite on to the tripod, the parallel plates should be equidistant, and the foot screws all set to the same length (another little wrinkle which will save a lot of time and obviate resetting the plummet when it comes to levelling up).

When everything is satisfactory between the centre of the peg and the plummet, the instrument may be levelled up in exactly the same way as previously described for the three-screw dumpy level. There is one exception, i.e., the bubble, instead of being on the telescope, is fixed to the top plate (some instruments

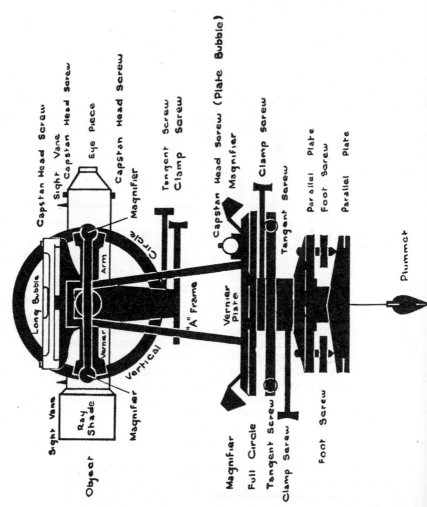

FIG. 61

have two, fixed at right angles to each other), the plate bubble is revolved until it is parallel to any two foot screws, brought half to the centre, the telescope reversed, and finally levelled.

The plate bubble is then turned over the remaining footscrew (which up to now should not have been touched), and the process repeated, using this screw only.

Finally slowly revolve the whole instrument, when the bubble should remain in the centre of its run. Now look to your plummet once more; if this is out of centre there is nothing for it but to shift the instrument slightly, and repeat the process of levelling with the foot screws until exactitude is obtained. Practice and observation will soon enable you to master this somewhat tedious operation.

Foremen who have an instrument with a centring attachment will find their work considerably lightened. The theodolite may be levelled and then centred without seriously disturbing the adjustment.

The lower and upper plates or circles (which carry the degree circle and Vernier respectively) are each controlled by two screws, a clamp and a tangent or slow motion. The clamp brings the plates as near as possible by eye to the required division, whilst the slow motion gives an exact adjustment.

The lower plate may be clamped in any position, the telescope revolved and sighted, and finally the top plate clamped to the lower to act as one, or the plates may be manipulated singly. The slow motion screw cannot, of course, be brought into play until its respective clamp screw has been tightened. Make it a habit to look at the clamp screw first before using the telescope.

Another important rule is: Always read the circle in one direction only; clockwise, with the arrow at zero. During the course of the work glance occasionally at the plate bubble to ensure that you are not out of level.

When sighting on to a rail or staff, tilt the telescope to the foot (just sufficient to clear grass or twigs or building debris) in order to avoid the error resulting from the staff being out of plumb as indicated in Fig. 62. It is obvious that by directing the cross hairs to the foot of the staff any swing outwards at the head of the staff is discounted.

The foreman or agent in using the theodolite is out to obtain the opposite result of the surveyor or engineer who made the original survey and designed the works or buildings.

Let us suppose that it is desired to set out an angle of 17 deg. 40 min. 20 sec. The surveyor, in making his original survey did not know what the angle was until he read it from his theodolite; there was nothing there except bare fields and hedges. He had to put his staff up, station himself over a survey peg, and so read the angle. This knowledge the surveyor passes on to the engineer who incorporates it in his drawings, and eventually gives it into the hands of the contractor who has to set out the angle previously found, namely 17 deg. 40 min. 20 sec.

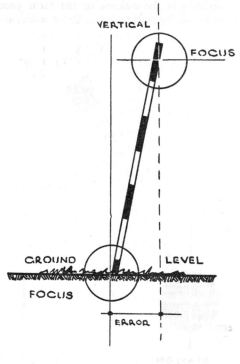

OUT OF VERTICAL

FIG. 62

Set the Vernier to zero, clamp both plates together and sight on to the peg making one arm of the angle. Turn through 17 deg. and note the arrow on the vernier. Next, by means of the slow motion screw, turn through two intermediate divisions on the main scale; the instrument will now be reading 17 deg. 40 min. 0 sec. Lastly by a further recourse to the tangent screw read the Vernier to 20 sec. and insert a peg.

Now read the opposite Vernier when the reading should show a difference of 180 deg. exactly. If it does not, go back to the first Vernier, look along the scale when you might find that two divisions seem to coincide in such a way that you are unable to say which division is the nearest or the most accurate. In these circumstances (if the setting out calls for extreme accuracy)

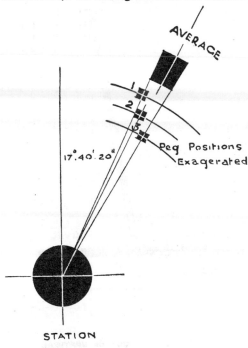

Fig. 63

you can set out the angle three times, inserting three pegs according to the readings and striking an average line as suggested in Fig. 63.

Set off the first angle of 17 deg. 40 min. 20 sec. as already described, clamp the two plates together. Then unclamp the lower plate and swing the two plates to the target so that the cross hairs of the telescope are set to start at 17 deg. 40 min. 20 sec., reset and read again through an angle of 35 deg. 20 min. 40 sec. and insert the second peg.

Use the second reading as your zero for the third sight and set out your angle once more, which this time should read 53 deg. 1 min. 0 sec. and insert the final peg.

A piano wire stretched between these pegs will give an extremely accurate setting out.

A surveyor employs a somewhat similar technique to determine an angle. The process may be repeated as many times as may be expedient, always bearing in mind, of course, the degree of accuracy required.

A hint may be given here that if you are using a Vernier instrument reading to 20 sec. no advantage will be obtained by trying to estimate by eye to 5 sec.

The same procedure may, of course, be used to obtain an extremely accurate setting out of a right angle. For the general run of work it is sufficient to set up the theodolite with the Vernier set to zero and swing through 90 deg. But in the case of very long shots where absolute exactitude is the aim, the surveyor should commence at any reading of the Vernier, say 23 deg. 45 min. 40 sec.

A right angle set off from this at a first reading should give a result of 113 deg. 45 min. 40 sec. Using this answer to obtain a second reading, the arrow should point to 203 deg. 45 min. 40 sec. For a third reading 293 deg. 45 min. 40 sec. and for a fourth reading (thus completing a full turn of 360 deg.) the Vernier should obviously point to 23 deg. 45 min. 40 sec.

It should be emphasised that this method should only be resorted to when extreme accuracy is required.

The reasoning behind this method is that inequalities in the instrument due to manufacture are eliminated, as are inaccuracies in the calibration of the circles and Verniers.

A variation of this method is to take any four readings of

90 deg. Commencing with your arrow pointing to, say, 4 deg. 10 min. 0 sec. read 94 deg. 10 min. 0 sec. You may then alter the reading of the circle to, say, 42 deg. 20 min. 20 sec. and swing the telescope to read 132 deg. 20 min. 20 sec., and so on. Of course, if at the second reading the cross hairs come exactly on to the centre of the first peg there is no need to proceed further.

So much for the setting out of angles, but it is just as important to know how to set out a straight line. A straight line of considerable length may be set out by ranging rods alone, but the method is dependent on the eye of the surveyor.

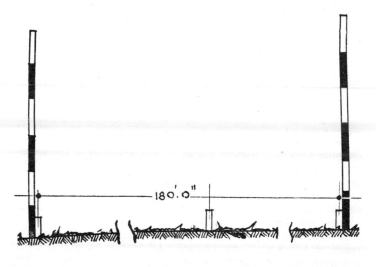

Fig. 64

Pegs may be set close up to and axially with the poles, as shown in Fig. 64, the rods then being withdrawn; a line or a succession of lines is then stretched from the end peg from a nail or notch in the head of the peg, and the centre of each peg marked in thick pencil where the line cuts.

For certain classes of work this is not accurate enough (say a long line of stanchions or reinforced concrete pillars). It is found that the centres so obtained are always a little to one side of the other, necessitating adjustments here and there at the final placing of the stanchion or shuttering for the concrete pillars.

The slight error arises from the fact that the work has been set out by the unaided eye and the centres of the pegs marked from one side or the other of the line. The use of a theodolite eliminates this difficulty.

PEG

NAIL

STATION

Fig. 65

There are three methods for setting out a straight line with a theodolite. Commencing operations, Fig. 65 shows the instrument set up at the beginning or end of the line to the exact angle required with both plates clamped. The engineer sights through telescope, elevating or depressing as required, whilst his assistant inserts stout pegs (which should be not less than 2in. square) according to the signals given and at suitable intervals along the line.

When the pegs are driven exactly and firmly to their final setting, the assistant draws a diagonal on the head of the peg and points the pencil to the centre so obtained. The surveyor then returns to his telescope and signals to the assistant once more if the sight gives an exact coincidence with the cross hairs, and if all is correct, a nail is driven in at the exact spot.

It seldom happens that the nail coincides exactly with the centre obtained from the first diagonals, the nail head generally being very slightly away from the crossed pencil lines. The nails used should, of course, have broad flat heads and in turn should have diagonals marked on them with a steel scriber. Finally concrete the peg in position.

You now have a centre which is really accurate. This procedure need not be repeated for every peg, but at every 100ft. or so, the intermediate legs being lined in by piano wire.

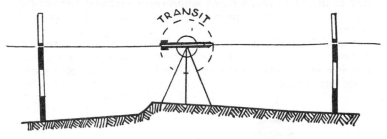

FIG. 66

The next method is more or less a repeat of the first, except that the theodolite, instead of being set up at the commencement or end of the line, is centred mid-way as indicated in Fig. 66, the telescope being either turned through 180 deg. (azimuth) or transitted, that is turned completely over on the vertical axis, so that the bubble (if it is attached to the telescope) appears underneath. This method should cancel out small errors in the manufacture of the instrument.

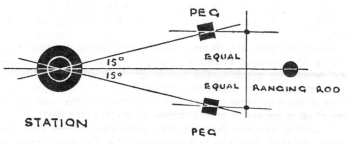

FIG. 67

The third method, shown in Fig. 67, gives extremely accurate results as it may be checked by means of the first method.

The theodolite is set up over a peg which is placed at the commencement or end of the line and the telescope is rotated through an angle (in full degrees for preference) and a ranging rod set up to one side of the proposed line.

Assume that an angle of 15 deg. is chosen. A similar angle is set out on the other side of the main line and a corresponding ranging rod is inserted in the ground, leaving the surveyor with two equally diverging arms on each side of his proposed main line.

With a 100ft. steel tape, and measuring from the centre of the instrument, an isosceles triangle is set out of which the two main arms are each 100ft. (or longer if possible) and the subtended angle is 30 deg. The extent of the arms is marked by inserting a peg, sighting through from the instrument, as already described. The distance between the pegs is now measured with the steel tape, thus giving a perpendicular from the centre of the base to the apex of the isosceles triangle, which is, of course, the centre of the instrument. The theodolite may now be moved to the other end of the line, when the cross hairs should bisect a ranging pole set up at the base to the isosceles triangle. Should a slight discrepancy be apparent, the distance should be carefully measured and averaged, the final peg being set to the marking so obtained.

The use of the theodolite in setting out building and civil engineering work is confined almost exclusively to the horizontal or azimuth circle, the vertical circle is less frequently used.

The surveyor, on the other hand, makes considerable use of the vertical circle when engaged in tacheometry, that is the calculation of horizontal distances from the centre of the instrument, without actual measurement and at the same time recording the relative heights or levels taken. A foreman would rarely be called on to carry out this intricate branch of theodolite work.

Slopes and gradients for banks and cuttings may, of course, be set out directly with the vertical circle, but this sort of work is far better effected by the use of the dumpy level.

The theodolite may be used for taking levels in the following manner.

Set up the instrument as described for using the azimuth circle with the vertical Vernier arc set to zero as near as possible. Turn the telescope slowly round (without reference to the telescope bubble) and look closely at the zero indication in all angles of light, slightly adjusting with the tangent screw until the position appears perfect; the plate bubbles must be set perfectly in the first instance, of course.

Now, reading the telescope bubble, adjust as for the dumpy level by turning the bubble parallel to any pair of foot screws, levelling up, and finally turning the telescope over the remaining foot screw. In all these operations bring the bubble half way with the foot screws, reverse the level and bring bubble to centre, making the smallest adjustment to the bubble itself by means of the capstan headed screws.

So far, so good: If it were a dumpy level we were using we could now go ahead secure in the knowledge that the instrument was set dead level. We cannot take this for granted with the theodolite. The telescope itself is mounted on trunnions, but it does not follow that the horizontal axis which passes through the two arms and the centre of the telescope is level, as may be seen in Fig. 68.

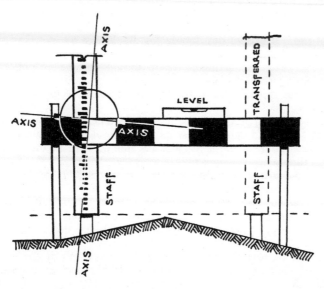

Fig. 68

H

There is also the secondary consideration that even if the trunnions are level, the diaphragm itself may not be level. These two errors may be ascertained in practically one simple operation.

Set up a sight rail at 200ft. distance from the instrument and level this in perfectly by means of an engineer's plate spirit level. The sight rail should be about 6ft. long. With the aid of a Sopwith staff placed against the back of the sight rail take two readings (which may be above or below the rail).

At each extremity of the rail the indicated height should be exactly the same when read from a level surface or two previously levelled pegs.

If there is a discrepancy and the main bubble rests in the centre of its run, the trunnions are not quite level and must be adjusted by means of the screw or capstan headed nut. The reading in each instance must be taken exactly on the crossing of the stadia lines.

Having made this adjustment it is now possible to test the setting of the diaphragm itself. Unclamp the circle and lower or raise the telescope (the bubble does not matter this time) until the horizontal stadia line coincides exactly with the top edge of the sight rail. If it does not, loosen the diaphragm by means of the capstan headed screws and revolve the frame slightly until the required result is obtained. There should now be no difficulty in resetting the telescope, not forgetting to clamp the vertical circle once more. The instrument is now set for use in taking levels.

It will be appreciated from this description that it is far better to use a dumpy level or a precise level to ascertain levels, the preparation of the theodolite for this purpose taking up too much time.

The old adage that "practice makes perfect" is never truer than in the use of the theodolite.

A foreman's use of the instrument is more or less restricted to the reading of the azimuth circle, and the setting out of right angles, so that it is a waste of time to delve too deeply into the realms of trigonometry. To confine oneself to the matter in hand and to ignore non-essentials is three-quarters of the battle in most matters concerning building works, especially the technical side.

A thorough knowledge of trigonometry is of importance in

larger works concerned with the setting out of bridges, viaducts, harbour works, tunnels and dams, but this involved work is invariably entrusted to professional surveyors and engineers, generally working in collaboration.

Whilst the foreman might be allowed to carry out theodolite work on small localised portions of such an undertaking, the engineers would take complete control of the main base line and preliminary triangulation.

The great thing is to assimilate the theory of the Vernier and to become so used to its working that you can with ease commence at any point on the circle and read it without going back to zero.

Chapter VIII

READING THE VERNIER SCALE

EVEN an experienced land surveyor will admit that reading a Vernier scale is difficult at the commencement and calls for ample and continuous practice before certainty and fluency can be attained.

Next to a dumpy level, the theodolite is the most useful of all instruments to a builder; yet how many builders possess one?

It is an instrument with many different and important usages. Setting out right angles for buildings of extreme length, long lines of kerbs, circles and parts of circles to large radii (say from 300 to 1,000ft.) where the centres are inaccessible or it is impossible to use a trammel, setting out curved roads on housing estates, large reservoirs or ornamental swimming pools, lining in centres of stanchions and piles, setting out lines of sewers and water mains (especially when there are no fixed points from which to start) and lining in tunnels, culverts and bridge abutments.

All these operations necessitate the use of a theodolite, but the supposed difficulty of reading the Vernier scale prevents most builders from undertaking their own theodolite work.

In the case of the dumpy level, a little intelligent study (which one may well indulge by oneself without the aid of an instructor) and a reasonable amount of practice, brings proficiency in reading and use within a comparatively short time.

With the theodolite it is different. The difficulty does not lie in the setting up of the instrument and its various adujstments, but in reading the Vernier scale. Once this difficulty is overcome (and it is only a passing difficulty) no builder who has once used a theodolite, and experienced the ease, efficiency and certainty of setting out by its means, will ever be without one again.

A land surveyor seldom works to an accuracy of less than ten seconds, and in many cases to a single second, or even half a second. A building contractor is never called upon to work to these refinements; in fact, a Vernier reading to one minute is more than sufficient for the generality of a builder's work, even for setting out steelwork or curves of large radius where the centre is out of reach. A civil engineer on the other hand finds that a circle which can be read to 20 seconds meets every demand of his work.

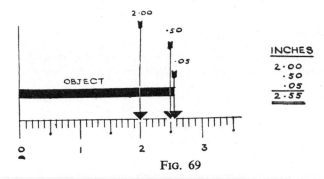

FIG. 69

As a preliminary it would be a good idea if we take an ordinary boxwood rule such as is used in schools, select the edge divided into tenths of an inch and measure the length of some small object as in Fig. 69. It will be found that we can judge fairly accurately by eye alone what the measured length is. It is easy to see that the length is (approximately) as follows:—

> 2·00 Read from scale.
> ·50 ,, ,, ,,
> ·05 Judged by eye.
>
> 2·55 inches.

Consideration in greater detail of the operation just carried out shows that the first two measurements, namely 2·00 and ·50 read direct from the scale are absolute certainties, but the last figure might easily be ·04 or ·06 *as near as we can judge;* having said that, we are not so certain now that it is ·05. True, in this instance, the error seems very small in either case, but if we were reading angular measurements from an instrument, it would be very large.

Assuming that the object measured in Fig. 69 is a piece of steel accurately machined to 2·57in. in length, it is at once apparent that all the guesses at the small fraction over ·50 were wrong, and that the eye is not to be trusted.

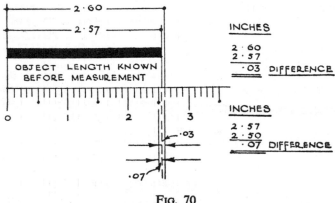

FIG. 70

Now look at Fig. 70, where the object, whose length is now known exactly (because we are told beforehand that it is so), is set out once more against the scale of one-tenths inches. A lot is to be learned from this, and we are now well on the way to understanding the Vernier scale.

Ignore the length of the object for the moment, and read to the next whole tenth of an inch; the reading is 2·60. The length of the object (which we already know to be 2·57in.) deducted from 2·60 leaves us with a remainder of ·03. By comparing one measurement with another we have been enabled to measure three-hundredths of an inch; not by inspection, but by an exact mathematical calculation.

Alternatively, we can take the last whole division immediately behind the steel bar, that is 2·50, and deduct this from the known length of the bar, when we find that we have been enabled to measure accurately ·07 of an inch. If only the bar had been machined to measure 2·59in., by the same process we could have measured to one-hundredth of an inch.

The process could be adapted in such a way that it would be possible to measure any fraction of an inch, centimetre or millimetre with mathematical accuracy.

This is exactly what Pierre Vernier, a French mathematician of the 16th century, thought, and he perfected the system of measurement of small fractions which bears his name and is used to-day in all scientific instruments requiring great accuracy of measurement.   The device is sometimes called a "Nonius", especially in Germany, where the prior claim of a Portuguese professor by the name of Pedro Nuñez who died in 1577 is sometimes considered.

Whatever the merits of the question might be, there is no denying that these two learned men, born so long ago, gave the world of science the most useful device for measuring extremely small fractions that has ever been thought of.

NINE DIVISIONS ON MAIN SCALE

TEN DIVISIONS ON VERNIER

FIG. 71

The actual construction of the scale, as conceived by Pierre Vernier, is depicted in Fig. 71. It will be seen that nine divisions on the main scale are equal to 10 divisions on the Vernier, so that the divisions on the latter must be only nine-tenths of those on the main scale.

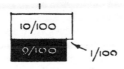

FIG. 72

If any division (selected at random) on the Vernier is placed immediately under any division on the main scale as in Fig. 72 (much magnified) the overlapping piece is equal to one-tenth of the main graduation, two divisions so placed are equal to two-tenths, and so on. In the example in Fig. 72, if the main scale is divided into tenths of an inch, one-tenth of it reads to one-hundredth of an inch; if the main division were equal to one-hundredth of an inch, the Vernier reading would give one-thousandth of an inch. Thus any degree of fineness may be obtained according to the unit chosen for the main scale.

A useful word might be said here about the micrometer which, by the way, is also used in a most ingenious manner in the construction of theodolites, giving spectacular results down to such fine limits as one second of arc, or even half a second. The Vernier is a totally different instrument, both in theory and construction, although the two methods are sometimes combined but this need not be considered for our purpose.

The micrometer is a very early 17th century invention by William Gascoign, a Yorkshire astronomer and mathematician, who obtained unheard of degrees of accuracy in his angular measurements. The micrometer instanced in this article (while made to the exact principle of the first invention) is not the instrument as used by William Gascoign, but the useful little pocket device as used by engineers to-day.

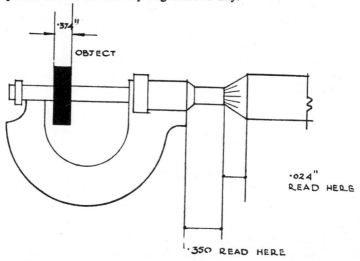

FIG. 73

The micrometer and its method of reading differs radically from that of the Vernier scale. The micrometer, which is mostly used in engineering work to measure the thickness of metals to exceedingly fine limits (one-thousandth of an inch, sometimes even one ten-thousandth), consists generally of a pair of steel jaws with accurately machined faces. The jaws open by means of a screw, the screw itself forming one mandible of the jaws. A piece of metal or other object, whose thickness it is necessary to obtain very accurately, is placed within the jaws of the micrometer as shown in Fig. 73 and the instrument is screwed up until it feels just right to the touch.

A micrometer screw reads direct. It is cut with 40 threads to the inch, so that one complete turn of the screw opens the jaws a distance of ·025in., or four complete turns equal one-tenth of an inch. The divisions are engraved on the shank of the instrument and generally numbered every fourth division, so that every numbered graduation denotes one-tenth of an inch; but supposing there is only a partial turn of the screw, how can we measure that? This is where the ingenious method of the micrometer comes into its own

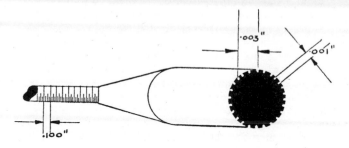

CREW THREAD CUT 40 = 1 INCH   EXPANDED AS SHEWN (EXAGGERATED)
ENABLES PARTIAL TURNS OF
MICROMETER SCREW TO BE READ

DIAGRAM SHEWING PRINCIPLE OF
MICROMETER

FIG. 74

The end of the screw is (in effect) widened out as in Fig. 74, so that the base is much larger than the original diameter of the main screw. It is now a comparatively easy operation to divide the circumference of the large circle thus obtained into 25 equal parts, and engrave them as numbered divisions. One complete turn of the micrometer screw is equal to ·025in., but the turn itself has now been divided into 25 equal parts, so that if the screw is turned ever so slightly through one division, we obtain one twenty-fifth of ·025, which is obviously ·001 or one-thousandth of an inch.

The micrometer might be summed up as an ingenious mechanical contrivance for measuring minute fractions *direct*. There is practically no mathematical theory in the micrometer although it is an extraordinarily clever invention, but (for those who are interested in such things) it is not to be compared for mathematical finesse with the Vernier scale.

We are now ready to make a start on the actual Vernier as used on a theodolite. The first thing to remember is that the scale of ten no longer holds good for reckoning purposes, but a scale of sixty. Scientific instrument makers designate this the sexagesimal system to differentiate it from the centesimal system where the circle, instead of being divided into 360 deg., is divided into 100 grades in each quadrant, or 400 for the complete circle.

Addition is performed not by counting "seven, eight, nine, ten, and carry one," but saying "fifty-seven, fifty-eight, fifty-nine, sixty, carry one."

The angular measurements used on a theodolite circle are in graduations of 60 seconds equal one minute, 60 minutes equal one degree, and 360 degrees make the complete circle.

Degrees are denoted by a numeral carrying as index a small circle, thus $10°$ (ten degrees); minutes by a numeral and a single dash as index, thus $10'$ (ten minutes); seconds by a numeral and two dashes as index, thus $10''$ (ten seconds). The complete reading would be $10°—10'—10''$.

Since we are no longer using a scale of ten, but one of 60, three and a half degrees is not written $3\frac{1}{2}°$ or $3·50°$, but $3°—30'$. Similarly three and a half minutes would be written $3'—30''$.

Notice how important it is to bear in mind constantly that all workings are to a scale of sixty. Reconsider the example just chosen of three and a half degrees and then three and a half minutes. Thirty minutes is half a degree, and 30 seconds is half a minute; that is, half of the half, which in the scale of ten would be a quarter, giving the result $3·00 + ·50 + ·25 = 3·750$.

We are, however, using the scale of sixty. In decimals the correct result would be $3·00, ·500, ·0083, 3·5083$; the reason being that 30 seconds is not a quarter of a degree (half of a half) but is the fraction $\dfrac{30}{60 \times 60} = \dfrac{1}{120} = ·0083$.

For a commencement it is as well to ignore the Vernier and to familiarise ourselves with reading the full circle which, on the actual instruments, is always read by means of a powerful magnifying glass or microscope. The engraved divisions and figures show up splendidly in a good light, and for straight-forward reading of the circle it is considerably easier than reading the inverting telescope on a level.

There are three main types of circle, reading to 30 minutes, 20 minutes and 10 minutes, all of which may be sub-divided, by inspection to half these amounts.

In the three diagrams Figs. 75-77, the three types are given (much magnified) where it will be noticed that each degree is divided into half, three and six respectively.

Specimen readings are indicated by the arrow heads on the diagrams for each type of circle; the last reading in each case being estimated by inspection.

Theodolites are manufactured with circles of various diameters; as small as $3\frac{1}{2}$in. and as large as 8in. for the most accurate land surveying. For the general builder and civil engineering contractor a 5in. diameter circle is ample. This gives a graduation of a bare twenty-fifth of an inch for one degree.

In Fig. 75, showing a reading of 30′ on the main circle, each division would measure scarcely 1/25th inch and the half division 1·50th and so on descending to Fig. 77 where the main circle reads to 10′ which would measure 1/140th inch on a 5in. diameter circle. (All the fractions given here are only very approximate.)

These exceedingly small divisions cause no trouble in reading. Modern instruments are supplied with most excellent microscopes.

If it were required to read the last division to 10″ instead of 10′ it would be necessary to divide this small graduation by sixty (remember we are in the scale of sixty); the portion of arc measuring 1/140th inch would thus become 1/8,400th inch. A microscope could easily pick this up, of course, but it would be quite a different matter engraving lines so fine and close together on a piece of metal or glass, making each line radiate exactly from a common centre.

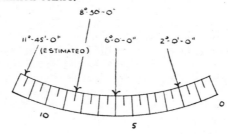

CIRCLE READING TO 30'

FIG. 75

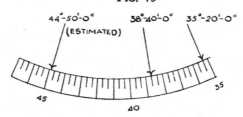

CIRCLE READING TO 20'

FIG. 76

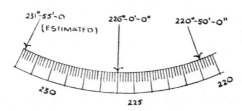

CIRCLE READING TO 10'

FIG. 77

The Vernier does all this for us in a most marvellous manner without making impossible demands on machine technique and the art of the engraver.

Refer once more to Figs. 75-77, and notice particularly the last reading in each case, which is given as "estimated". This implies that we have been able to read direct from the main circle with absolute certainty (taking the last reading on Fig. 75 as an example) the angular measurement of 11°—30′—0″, but the remaining 15′ we have estimated by eye alone. Looking at the circle the arrow appears to point exactly midway between a half division, so that when reading the actual instrument 15′ would require us to judge by eye alone a bare 1/100th inch. The pointer might easily be at 16′ or 14′ or even 17′ or 13′. A most difficult measurement to assess by inspection. When we come to Fig. 77 reading to 10′ the arrow might indicate 231°—55′—0″ or anywhere between 53′ and 57′.

Why trouble to measure these extremely small fractions of a degree? Surely it would make little or no difference on the actual job; a discrepancy of two or three minutes, bearing in mind that there might possibly be compensating errors?

On work of small dimensions, where the walls or run of joists do not exceed 50ft. in length, an error of even five minutes would probably make no great difference, but then you would not need the aid of a theodolite.

In the case of a factory building with flank walls 600ft. long with steel stanchions built in at 20ft. centres, bracketed to take a first floor and roof trusses over, an error of one minute setting out from the main corner peg would amount to just over 2in. which in turn would throw everything out; floor joists, intermediate girders and roof trusses. It is therefore very important to be able to read with exactitude very small angular measurements.

A simple demonstration of this is to draw a circle 5in. in diameter and draw two radii so close together that they appear parallel. Using the same centre, circumscribe another circle, say, 20in. diameter, and project the same two radii. It will be seen at once with what rapidity the minute divergence of the radii increases as the radius of the circle is enlarged. (This increase in divergence is, in reality, a chord and is strictly proportionate to the length of the radius and the included angle at the centre;

a fact of the greatest importance and use to civil engineers and land surveyors when setting out curves.)

We are now prepared to tackle the Vernier arm itself. The example chosen as depicted in Fig. 78 shows a Vernier scale reading to 10″ or 1/360th of a degree.

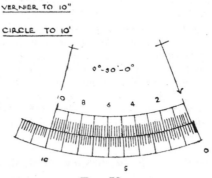

FIG. 78

It is now more important than ever to remember that we are in the scale of 60. If we look very carefully at the diagram it will be noticed that the arrow head of the Vernier arm points to one small division past zero on the main scale, and further, that the 10 on the Vernier arm and the 10 on the main scale coincide.

Each degree is divided into six smaller divisions each of which, therefore, gives a reading of 10′. The theodolite in this example is therefore reading an angle of 10′.

Another peculiarity emerges from this example. It will be noticed that 60 small divisions on the Vernier arm exactly equal 59 small divisions on the main scale, which is equivalent to taking the small division (coloured black in Fig. 78) splitting it into 60 equal parts and deducting one part so obtained from each division on the Vernier arm.

Following up our analysis we find that if the small division, filled solid black in Fig. 78, represents an angular measurement of 10′, then splitting it into 60 equal parts gives an angular measurement of 10″, which is the greatest measure of accuracy required of this particular instrument.

Refer once more to Fig. 72. If the white division, instead of representing 10/100ths of an inch, represented one minute, and the lower black division, instead of measuring 9/100ths of an inch, measured 50 *seconds* (60″—10″) we should arrive at the fraction of 10″ shown overlapping.

The main characteristic of the Vernier arm as used on theodolites is that it reads to the nearest large division and deducts the corresponding smaller measurement, the difference being the fraction sought, in this case 10″ and its multiples.

Each division on the lower scale is equal to ten minutes which equals six hundred seconds.

Each division on the Vernier scale is equal to nine minutes fifty seconds (600″—10″) which produces the following equation:—

Main Scale .. .. 59 × 600 Seconds
Vernier Arm .. .. 60 × 590 Seconds

There is no need to work this out as it can be seen at a glance that they are equal.

A theodolite reading to 20″ has the following equation:—

Main Scale .. .. 59 × 1200 Seconds
Vernier Arm .. .. 60 × 1180 Seconds

This expression is not so easy to see at a glance, but when multiplied out it will be found that they are equal.

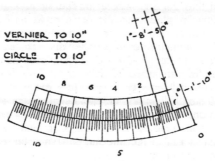

FIG. 79

Now as a check on the method let us take the example shown in Fig. 79, reading 1°—1′—10″.

The angle of 1° causes no trouble in reading. It can be seen by inspection of the main scale. It is the very small fraction of 1′—10″ which needs some explanation.

If we look along the Vernier scale we note that the first division that exactly coincides with a division on the main scale (shown by the radial lines in the diagram) occurs 2°—10′—0″ from zero, corresponding to seven divisions of the Vernier.

We already know that each division on the Vernier arm equals 9′—50″, so that seven divisions equal 4130 seconds, or 1°—8′—50″. Deduct this from 2°—10′—0″ on the main scale and we have the required answer 1°—1′—10″.

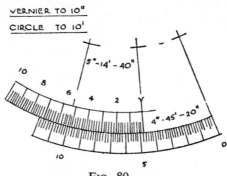

FIG. 80

Now proceed to Fig. 80 where a reading of 4°—45′—20″ is indicated. Counting along the Vernier arm we note that 32 divisions coincide exactly with 10 large divisions on the main scale. The task of reading is thus simplified. It is thus merely 10°—0′—0″ less (32 × 9′—50″) or 18,880 seconds. Multiplied out in the scale of sixty the full expression is as follows:—

$$10°—0′—0″ - 5°—14′—40″$$
$$= 4°—45′—20″.$$

Once the mathematical basis of the whole operation is thoroughly understood, reading a Vernier scale with accuracy and assurance becomes easy. All one has to remember is that a large reading is deducted from one slightly larger in order to obtain a very small remainder, which would be very difficult otherwise to read.

If we now look at Fig. 81 we see that a very small division on the main scale is (by the aid of Pierre Vernier's wonderful invention) in effect magnified to the large set of divisions on the Vernier arm.

There are three main types of circle on theodolites; some read from 0 to 90 and have four similar quadrants; others read 90, 180, 270 and 360 or a variation of this; but whatever system is chosen you are safe in the knowledge that they all add up to 360°. The direct reading of the circle causes no difficulty.

Fig. 81

Modern instruments are calibrated with surprising accuracy; the larger the diameter of the circle the greater the accuracy. Astronomical telescopes have an enormous circle, many of the very earliest astronomical telescopes possessing a circle in which the degree measured no less than 4in. across, making a full diameter of 120ft. With such an instrument (although devoid of telescope or microscope) it was possible to read to unprecedented degrees of accuracy, even to decimals of a second.

For general surveying and setting out works it is, of course, impossible to carry about with one an instrument with a very large circle, hence the necessity of using a theodolite with a small diameter circle and a means of reading it as accurately as possible.

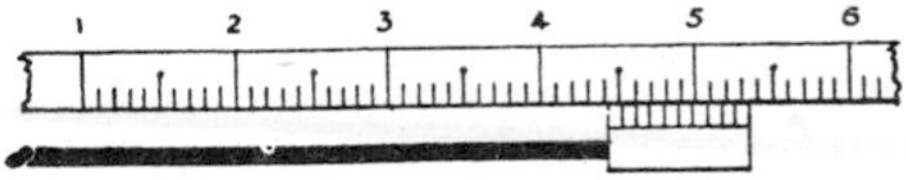

Fig. 82

To clinch the theory of the Vernier scale finally, let us end with one more proof; this time a purely mathematical one in the form of a simple equation. Fig. 82 shows an object measuring 4·42in. in length, read by a Vernier to 1/100 of an inch. It has to be proved that the fraction shown on the main scale as being the excess over ·40″ is equal to ·02″.

Starting with the known fact that 10 divisions on the lower

I

scale are equal to nine divisions on the upper scale, we arrive at the following simple equation:—

Let a = any number of divisions on the upper scale.

Let x = minute distance required to be measured.

$$(9/10a) + x = a$$
$$\therefore \quad x = a - (9/10a)$$
$$\therefore \quad x = a/10$$

But a equals 2 divisions each ·10 in length.

$$\therefore \quad a = \cdot20$$
$$\therefore \quad \frac{a}{10} = \cdot02$$

Total length of object = 4·40 + ·02 = 4·42.

Chapter IX

A GLIMPSE AT THE STEELWORK BOOK

A THOROUGH understanding of the steelwork book can save a contractor a large amount of money; it makes him independent of professional advice (and fees); it opens up ways and means of carrying out small structural alterations economically and expeditiously.

It may put work within his grasp which he might otherwise have lost just for the lack of ability to decide quickly and accurately how two buildings should be knocked into one, how to cut out a house front and instal a shop front, or how to erect a beam in a garage to carry hoist and tackle. In all these instances the client expects a builder to say "Yes" together with reasons and costs.

Waiting for an engineer's blue prints and estimates frightens the customer away; or he loses interest (in *you* at least), and goes to someone else who can give a confident affirmative within a couple of days.

The steelwork book meets all these contingencies. It only needs to be understood and read as intended. No further calculation is necessary once the groundwork is absorbed. The clever engineers who have compiled the tables have done the work for us. There is nothing left for us to do except to use our intelligence in applying the tables to the problem we have in hand.

The moment of inertia (see Chapter X) is simply the sum of every particle in the cross sectional area of a beam multiplied by the square of its distance from the neutral axis. The definition and property needs rendering down as it were into a more congenial form before it can be applied with ease to steelwork calculations.

This "inertia digest" (if I might coin a phrase) is called by engineers a "modulus of section" and is generally tabulated in the steelwork book after the values of the various moments of inertia. Maximum and minimum values for all moduli of sections are given.

Before explaining the calculations underlying the section moduli it will be necessary to deal with that most important item governing cost, namely weight, to which is closely bound the cross sectional area of the section.

Steel weighs 489·60lb. per cu. ft.

An ingot of steel 12in. long by 7½in. wide by 24in. deep would therefore weigh 612lb.; the maximum moment of inertia would be 8640·00.

A beam of these dimensions would carry a distributed load of 240 tons over a span of 20ft. using an extreme fibre stress of 10 tons to the square inch.

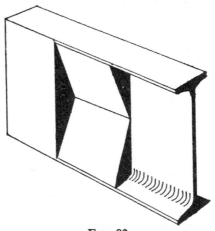

Fig. 83

Now let us take the same section of steel and whittle it down as shown in Fig. 83 until we have obtained the shape of an R.S.J. with flanges 7½in. wide and a total depth over the flanges of 24in. weighing 95lb. per foot run. From the tables this joist will carry a distributed load of 70·30 tons over a span of 20ft.

It would be possible to carry a distributed load of 421·80 tons over a span of 20ft. by placing six joists, each weighing 95lb. per foot run, side by side.

This manoeuvre confronts us with the surprising economic proposition that by careful design of the cross sectional area of a beam, it is possible to carry 181·80 tons more and yet save 42lb. per foot run of steel in the process.   The working is: 612lb. −6 (95lb.) = 42lb.

The cross sectional area of an R.S.J. is a most important thing and one which must be computed with the greatest possible accuracy.

Referring once more to Fig. 83 it is easy to see that if a cross sectional area size 7½in. × 24in. = 180 sq. in. corresponds to a weight of 612lb. for a length of one foot, then a 24in. × 7½in. R.S.J. should (according to the tables) give a weight of 95lb. per foot run.

The following working should therefore give the results shown in the tables:

$$\frac{\text{Area of R.S.J. (from tables)} \times \text{weight of solid ingot}}{\text{Area of solid ingot}} = \text{weight of R.S.J.}$$

$$\frac{27 \cdot 94 \times 612\text{lb.}}{180 \cdot 00} = 94 \cdot 99\text{lb.}$$

When working from a set of steelwork tables it should be mentioned that the cross sectional area and weights of various R.S.J. have been altered slightly from time to time as also the allowable safe working stresses.   Needless to say, this fact does not alter the principles of calculation of the laws of mechanics.   Any weights or loads taken from the older tables will in fact give a stronger resulting structure than the latest tabulated loads and stresses.

It is a purely a matter of opinion on what should be regarded as the factor of safety and convenience in the technical process of rolling.

As an instance of this the 24in. × 7½in. R.S.J. of our example. The 1928 tables give this joist as weighing 90lb. per foot run with a cross sectional area of 26·465 sq. in.: the 1932 tables list it as weighing 100lb. per foot lineal with a cross sectional area of 29·39 sq. in.   Finally the latest tables state a weight of 95lb. per foot run with a cross sectional area of 27·94 sq. in.

All these differences are rather confusing at first but they do not in any way affect the principles of steelwork calculation.   The working stresses in the first two instances are calculated at 8·00 tons per sq. in. extreme fibre stress, whilst the present day tables increase this to 10 tons.

The ultimate strength of structural steel does not exceed 32 tons per sq. in. so it would appear there is a considerable reduction in the factor of safety in present day work; on the other hand it might be considered as a considerable increase in the quality of steel manufactured.

The tables themselves, however, are rather against this latter conjecture as revealed when it comes to the study of deflection. In actual practice, the rolling mills cannot guarantee that their steelwork sections (joists, angles, tees, channels, or flats) will equal the weights specified.

The weights are never less than specified, but may be in excess by as much as 2½ per cent., which excess is charged for. This is known as rolling margin.

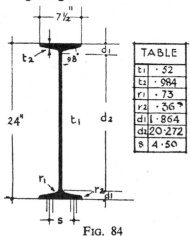

TABLE	
t_1	·52
t_2	·984
r_1	·73
r_2	·36
d_1	1·864
d_2	20·272
s	4·50

FIG. 84

In terms of money, on a nominal weight of 10 tons of structural steel at say £40 per ton delivered on site this would involve an extra charge of £10 exclusive of the extra weight to be handled and fixed into position. An important desiderata often overlooked.

The shape and weight of a H-section girder is the finest example in the whole field of building and civil engineering of how to use a material to its best advantage, structurally and from the point of view of cost.

Using our first example of a 24in. × 7½in. R.S.J. the exact setting out is shown in Fig. 84. The earlier form of the section is chosen merely for convenience in the use of the tables at hand. The 1959 B.S.S. 449 is exactly the same except that the section is slightly larger in area.

Each constituent part of the section has been draughted in a special manner and the areas computed by a planimeter, or an actual section cut off, accurately machined, and weighed; either method giving the exact cross sectional area.

The setting out of the section, together with the indications used for each part of the joist is the accepted method used by steelwork engineers.

The shape of the section has an important bearing on understanding what follows. It is not necessary to undergo the fatigue of finding the moment of inertia every time we want to design a beam. The process may be simplified considerably by deriving a formula from the moment of inertia, and using that. It is a paradox of this type of calcuation that the various steps of simplification make the main idea more difficult to understand. Once this difficulty is obviated, all is plain sailing.

JOISTS, DIMENSIONS AND PROPERTIES

TABLE 1.   B.S. 449. REVISED, 1959

Size D x B in inches	Weight in lb. per foot	Area in Square Inches	Standard Thickness		Moments of Inertia		Section Moduli	
			Web	Flange	Axis X-X	Axis Y-Y	Axis X-X	Axis Y-Y
24 x 7½	95	27·94	·57	1·011	2533·04	62·54	211·09	16·68
20 x 6½	65	19·12	·45	·820	1226·17	32·56	122·62	10·02
16 x 6	50	14·71	·40	·726	618·09	22·47	77·26	7·49

Consult the typical steelwork tables as shown here, with several joists taken at random, commencing with the R.S.J. size 24in. × 7½in. × 95lb. per foot run.

The moment of inertia is listed as 2533·04. The corresponding modulus of section is given as 211·09. What is the connection between the two and how will it help us to find the strength of the beam?

If we were forced to work solely from the inertia value it

would entail a vast number of calculations for each fibre of steel according as the stress varied from its square of the distance from the neutral axis, which in turn would have to be multiplied by innumerable little lever arms from the neutral axis.

There is one way out of this difficulty. An average value of stress area multiplied by an average value of lever arm would solve the problem; that is exactly what a modulus of section is.

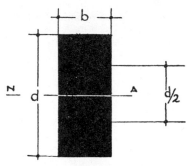

FIG. 85

Fig. 85 explains the proposition which now looks very simple, but isn't! We know that we must have two things to start with: (a) an average stress area and (b) an average lever arm. There is yet a third requisite to be brought into play: (c) an average stress value.

Referring again to Fig. 85, it appears that the average lever arm will obviously be equal to half the depth of the beam, which is d/2. This depth divided into the moment of inertia should produce the required result, the average stress area, in other words the modulus of section.

Take two examples as a test.

> 24in. × 7½in. R.S.J. maximum
> moment of inertia 2533·04
> Half depth of beam or d/2 = 12in.
> Divide d/2 into maximum moment of inertia
>
> $$\frac{2533\cdot04}{12} = 211\cdot09$$

EXAMPLE 2

16in. x 6in. R.S.J. maximum
moment of inertia 618·09
Half depth of beam or $d/2 = $ 8in.
Divide $d/2$ into maximum moment of inertia

$$\frac{618·09}{8} = 77·26$$

We now have an inkling of the meaning and use of modulus of section.

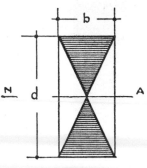

FIG. 86

Fig. 86 may be taken as the graphical representation of the variation in stress within the confines of a rectangular beam.

The shape of this diagram is very important. It consists of two inverted triangles within the beam obtained by the intersection of the diagonals, and indicates, in exact proportion, how the stress varies from the extreme compressive stress at the top of the section to zero at the neutral axis, then once more swelling out to the extreme tensional stress at the bottom of the beam.

The extreme importance of this diagram is that the shaded portion may be looked on as the virtual section if each component fibre of the beam were under full stress.

You will not fail to have noticed how the shaded area is approaching the shape of an R.S.J. It would not need much alteration of the profile to obtain the familiar H-section of a steel joist.

Before we can proceed further with this interesting speculation we must leave it for a few moments and concentrate on Fig. 87 whcih shows an isosceles triangle cut from a piece of stout cardboard and suspended from a pin. Mark the triangle out as accurately as possible, draw a line at right angles to the base through to the apex, measure the length of this line, and at a point two-thirds down from the apex or one-third up from the base, pierce with an ordinary pin.

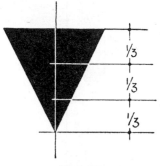

FIG. 87

Hold the cardboard triangle up as in Fig. 88 and it will be found that if the cardboard is slowly turned round with the free hand, the triangle will remain in whatever position it is put, whereas if the pin is thrust through any other portion of the triangle and then slowly turned, it will as surely fall back into its original position.

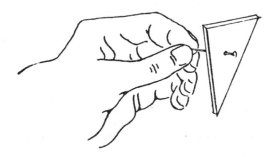

FIG. 88

This is a most important demonstration of the centre of gravity of the figure and must be fully appreciated to understand what follows.

In talking of the centre of gravity of a mere shape or area denoted by outline, it is not quite correct, the mathematical name being centroid, but for our purpose it is hardly necessary to talk with such precision.

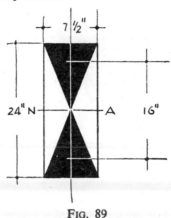

FIG. 89

Fig. 89 shows the subject matter of the three previous diagrams brought together.

It is now possible to verify what we have already propounded, by an actual numerical example.

The section modulus (which we are using for the first time) of a $7\frac{1}{2}$in. × 24in. beam should be as follows:—

(a) $\dfrac{7\frac{1}{2} \times 24}{4}$ = Area of two triangles representing compression and tension.

(b) $2(2/3 \times 12) = 16$ = Full length of lever arm.

(c) (a) × (b) = modulus of section.

$\dfrac{15 \times 24 \times 16}{2 \times 4} = 720 \cdot 00$ modulus of section.

The above working looks a little mysterious in view of the

fact that we have already stated (and proved by the steelwork tables) that the modulus of section is equal to the moment of inertia divided by half the depth of the section.

Check the calculation by this method.

$$\frac{bd^3}{12} = \frac{7\frac{1}{2} \times 24 \times 24 \times 24}{12}$$

Section modulus =

$$\frac{bd^3}{12} \text{ divided by } \frac{d}{2} = \frac{bd^2}{6}$$

$$\frac{bd^2}{6} = \frac{7\frac{1}{2} \times 24 \times 24}{6} = 720 \cdot 00 \text{ section modulus}$$

There is no need to check further. The reasoning is correct.

There now remains the question of the application of the modulus of section in order to be able to select a suitable beam. For this is required the permissible stress on the steel, both in tension and compression. Fortunately for steelwork engineers, the stress on steel for both these cases is equal, and so we are saved from the shamble of computation required for reinforced concrete work.

The permitted stress for steel is to-day given as 10 tons per sq. in. Prior to 1920 it was $7\frac{1}{2}$ tons per sq. in., when it was altered to 8 tons per sq. in.

It is important to note that working stress is only a fraction of ultimate or breaking stress, and is generally denoted in steelwork handbooks by a figure, as 4, 3·8, or even 3; the figure being known as the factor of safety.

Thus a factor of safety of 4 for a working stress of $7\frac{1}{2}$ tons means that the ultimate strength of the material is 30 tons per sq. in.

A factor of safety of 3·8 (as in most of the older books) still indicated an ultimate strength of 30 tons, which showed a permissible decrease in the factor of safety.

The term "factor of safety" is rather misleading to the tyro.

It does not mean safety for the designer to make a few well chosen errors. It must not be thought that because steel will take an ultimate stress of say 32 tons per sq. in. that a scheme is marvellously safe in working to 8 to 10 tons per sq. in. The designer in fact has nothing to play with and must keep scrupulously to the permitted stresses.

The factor of safety and the working stress are so calculated that they allow for hidden defects in the material itself during the course of manufacture; chemical, physical and mechanical. It allows for fatigue of the metal, diminution of section due to flawing and oxidation, and shortcomings of site construction.

Now that we are clear as to the meaning of working stress it is easy to see that all that remains to be done is to multiply the section modulus by the stress value as the following example shows: —

> From tables, section modulus of 24in. × 7½in.
> × 95lb. R.S.J. 211·09
> Working stress 10 tons per sq. in.
> Maximum distributed load for 1ft. span=
> 211·09 × 10 = 2110·9 tons.

Safe distributed load for a span of 10ft. = 211·09 tons. Check by the published Tables. The load given for a 10ft. span is only 140 tons. The discrepancy between the two workings is too large to neglect.

Refer to the isosceles triangle once more in Fig. 87 and remember that the value of the stress varies from a maximum to zero as it approaches the neutral layer. The reason for the error in our working is at once apparent. The average value of the working stress proves to be two thirds of 10 tons, which equals 6·66 tons per sq. in.

The required answer now becomes: section modulus 211·09 × 6·66 which equals 1395·30 tons over 1ft. span or 139·53 tons over 10ft. span; or 140 tons in round figures as shown in the tables.

In certain steelwork tables two other properties of R.S.Js are sometimes given; the safe distributed load on one foot span, and the maximum moment of resistance of a beam.

When taken in conjunction with the maximum moment of inertia, the section modulus, and the tabular distributed loads, these two extra items of information make for confusion until it is clear in our minds of the relationship between the properties.

The safe distributed load on one foot span is merely the value of the section modulus multiplied by the average permissible working stress.

The following three examples prove this: —

9in. × 4in. × 21lb. R.S.J.
Section modulus 18·00.
Average stress, 5·33 tons per sq. in.
18·00 × 5·33 = 96·00 tons.

18in. × 6in. × 55lb. R.S.J.
Section modulus 93·50.
Average stress, 5·33 tons per sq. in.
93·50 × 5·33 = 498·80 tons.

3in. × 1½in. × 4lb. R.S.J.
Section modulus 1·10.
Average working stress, 5·33 tons per sq. in.
1·10 × 5·33 = 5·90 tons.

You will note that in all the above examples the stress has been taken at 8 tons per sq. in. for the extreme fibres of the beam, which when related to the centre of the isosceles triangle becomes two-thirds of eight, or 5⅓ tons.

The great value in the above method of working is that the distributed load for any span is strictly proportional to the value for 1ft. 0in. span, as also a central concentrated load (which, of course, necessitates a joist twice as strong or a load of half the weight.)

Suppose it were required to find the exact distributed load which a 9in. × 4in. × 21lb. R.S.J. would support over a span of 8ft. 6in., it would only be necessary to divide the figure of 96 tons by 8½ to give the required answer, and thus save ourselves a lot of calculation.

The other method, of selecting a joist by the tabular maximum moment of resistance, is also very useful for structures slightly more involved than the class of work intended to be covered by this chapter, but nevertheless is a very useful thing to know, even for simple constructions.

Take an example at random from the tables: —

9in. × 7in. × 50lb. R.S.J., working stress 8 tons per sq. in., modulus of section 46·20, maximum moment of resistance 30·80 ft. tons.

If the above data are correct, the maximum of resistance should be able to be reduced to the equivalent of the section modulus.

Reduce maximum moment of resistance from ft. tons to in. tons and divide the result by 8.

$$\frac{30{\cdot}80 \times 12}{8} = 46{\cdot}20$$

There is one further important consideration in the design of a steel girder noted in the compilation of all steelwork tables— the incidence of vertical shear.

A beam that has an adequate modulus of section and is perfectly suitable in every other respect to resist flexure caused by the load imposed, may fail unexpectedly through shearing of the very metal itself.

In structural steelwork the action of shear is practically confined to downward or vertical shear, the superimposed load being so great that it causes the particles of steel to slide past each other, producing somewhat the effect of a heavy weight on a pile of planks, or the inverted sheaves of a railway carriage spring indicated in Figs. 90 and 91.

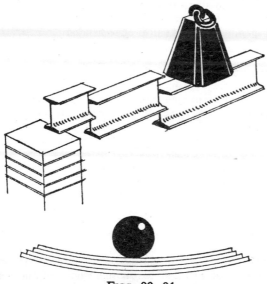

Figs. 90, 91

For our purpose we shall neglect the action of horizontal shear since its affects principally rivets, rivet pitch, and bearing values for compound girders.

In extreme cases a heavy load will so act that the effects of horizontal and vertical shear are combined, the two forces producing diagonal shear. This is a complication with which we shall not deal.

The builder, in the general run of his work, will not become enmeshed in design to this extent, but it is as well to know the possibilities, if only to guard against one's own lack of knowledge.

For all ordinary purposes the steelwork tables protect us against the effects of vertical shear.

When it comes to the larger spans and heavier girders the tabular loads are divided by a dotted zigzag line. All loads to the left of this line will produce vertical shear or web buckling or both if not stiffened in some way.

If therefore you find that the joist you have chosen falls to the left of the dotted line and bears a load equal to the tabular load, web support will be required and perhaps a thicker web, but these troubles are hardly likely to arise in a simple structure.

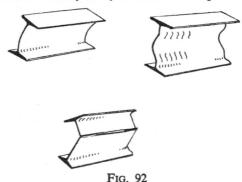

Fig. 92

Another word has crept in to trouble us, "web buckling". This is allied to shear but differs from it in that the beam may fail despite the fact of being able to resist shear. Some loads imposed on girders are so heavy by comparison with the depth of the web of the R.S.J. that the whole thing buckles up as though it were an overloaded strut. Fig. 92 gives an indication of three of the main forms which web buckling takes. The use of web stiffeners as in Fig. 93 combats this effect.

FIG. 93

The calculations involved are very laborious and call for a structural engineer's knowledge. Suffice it to say that in making calculations to ascertain the strength of a web, both as regards shear and buckling, the net depth and thickness of the web only are taken; the thickness of the flanges being neglected for this purpose.

Having ascertained the effective depth of the web, the correct stress to allow is obtained by treating the web as a small column and dividing the length by the radius of gyration to obtain a ratio of slenderness. There is one other important consideration before we can be content with the result of our investigations.

A beam may be perfectly safe and have met all the tests which we have so far applied and yet be unsuitable, due to the fact that after loading to its full capacity it gradually shows a marked deflection or sag, which is not only unsightly in itself but may damage neighbouring work.

Plaster ceilings, cased in beams, and false arches acquiring unsightly cracks, doors commence to jamb and windows stick. The client thinks the whole place is falling down. In actual practice conditions it must be remembered that a distributed load is not placed on a girder suddenly, or all at once.

First of all the beam is hoisted into position, then a few days later floor joists, or pre-cast hollow beams are laid across the top flange, later still the concrete units are grouted, then screeded, and eventually the ceiling is plastered, and finally the finished floor surface (possibly wood blocks) is laid; the whole process of

K

loading the girder is very gradual indeed. The deflection takes place imperceptibly.

In this way the deflection remains unnoticed until the building has been occupied for some months, when the final and full deflection occurs.

This extremely annoying occurrence can be avoided by calculating the full theoretical deflection which is likely to take place for any system of loading or span.

The calculations are laborious as the following formula shows, but if you keep within the heavy full black zig-zag line shown in the tables a lot of fatiguing mathematical work can be avoided.

MAXIMUM DEFLECTION AT CENTRE OF SPAN

$$dn = \frac{5W1^3}{348 \ EI}$$

dn = maximum deflection in inches.
W = weight or load in tons.
b = length of span in inches.
E = modulus of elasticity in tons per sq. in.
I = moment of inertia.

For a worked example let us take an 18in. × 6in. × 55lb. R.S.J. carrying a uniformly distributed load of 24·90 tons over a span of 20ft. 0in. Safe working stress 8 tons per sq. in.

This is the full tabular load. What will be the greatest amount of deflection at the centre of the beam?

$$dn = \frac{5W1^3}{348 \ EI}$$

W = 24·90 tons.
b = 20ft. 0in. = 240in.
E = 12,000 tons per sq. in.
I = 841·759

$$\frac{5 \times 24·90 \times 240 \times 240 \times 240}{348 \times 12,000 \times 841·759} = ·43in.$$

The working shows us that the deflection to be expected will be less than ½in. in a span of 20ft.; which may be taken as satisfactory.

To emphasise the importance of this deflection formula and the use of the full zig-zag line let us take the same joist but this time for a span of 40ft. 0in. with the full tabular distributed load of 12·40 tons.

The beam will be perfectly safe structurally, but in terms of deflection it would be disastrous as the following working shows:

$$\frac{5}{2} \times \frac{12\cdot40 \times 480 \times 480 \times 480}{384 \times 12{,}000 \times 841\cdot759} = 1\cdot76\text{in.}$$

It will therefore be appreciated that a sag of 13/4in. at the centre of the beam could not be tolerated. A stronger section would have to be chosen.

Knowing how to use a deflection formula is as important as calculating the bending moment. An undue deflection in a beam is apparent even to the eyes of the layman.

The appropriate Steelwork Tables may be obtained from THE BRITISH STANDARDS INSTITUTION, 2, PARK STREET, LONDON, W.1. The document to ask for is B.S.S. 449 (Revised 1959), "The Use of Structural Steel in Buildings". The relevant working instructions accompanying B.S.S. 449/1959 is "The British Standard Code of Practice No. CP. 113." The Structural Use of Steel in Buildings. Do not be confused by the similarity of the titles: the two documents are entirely separate and with distinct usages.

A useful guide to the design of steel framed buildings is *Steel Designers' Manual* (2nd edition, Crosby Lockwood, 50s.).

Chapter X

SELECTING THE GIRDER

BUILDERS are called upon to do many things which, strictly speaking, are outside the field of their normal activities, and, I suppose, the most frequently recurring of these demands is that of selecting a girder.

The design of structural steelwork in the case of an extensive scheme is generally given to a civil engineer, or to a firm of structural engineers who will not only design the whole fabric but also give a competitive tender. Should the contract go forward they will also prepare all plans, details and setting out instructions.

In the general run of building practice, however, many jobs are too small to warrant the employment of an engineer with the result that the builder is called upon himself to choose a girder suitable for the job.

In the case of a client who asks a builder for a minor alteration to be carried out (say the cutting of a 10ft. span opening in a brick wall in order to form a garage door) involving the use of one or more girders, the work is generally of moderate dimensions and limited cost, yet the technical work involved is equal in importance and intricacy to that in a large contract.

A lot of responsible work (generally unappreciated by the client because he is ignorant of it) devolves on the builder, work which is certainly totally outside the sphere and training of most builders, but which nevertheless has to be done.

The builder has recourse to his steelwork book, runs his finger down the tables until he comes to the appropriate span in feet (10ft. in the example cited) notes that a 9in. × 4in. × 21lb. R.S.J. will carry a distributed load of 9·61 tons, but plumps for a 10in. × 6in. × 42lb. R.S.J. which will carry 22·60 tons just to make certain; better safe than sorry.

It is generally stated in prominent type in the tables that the safe concentrated load at the centre is equal to half the distributed load. Beyond understanding this information and noting

148

the weight per foot lineal of the joist and its sectional area in square inches, the builders comprehends very little beyond this; not that he could not master it, but the subject has never been explained to him, yet it is one upon which he is constantly required to act.

There are many excellent text books on constructional steelwork, but without exception these are written for the student engineer and qualified practitioner, always with the tacit assumption that the reader is a senior wrangler. Opposed to this there are other treatises which are so simplified that they tell the reader nothing of the real problems to be solved and so are of less use than an advanced text book to an untrained mind.

Girders, beams, joists, and bressumers depend on one main factor for their strength (all other factors being entirely subsidiary) and it is the object of this chapter to explain to the reader what that chief and most important factor is so that he may choose a girder with certainty and confidence in any of the small jobs upon which he is called to act. He will certainly not be required to wrestle with the many complicated problems of steelwork construction which the qualified engineer is required to solve.

Steelwork tables for joists and beams are generally set out as the following example. Only the properties of the joists are shown here. The length of span in feet and the corresponding distributed loads are self explanatory and therefore do not need to be included.

TABLE 2.

Size D x B in inches	Weight in lb. per foot	Area in square inches	Moments of inertia		Section moduli		Span in feet
			Axis X-X	Axis Y-Y	Axis X-X	Axis Y-Y	3 4 5 6 etc.
9 x 4	21	6·18	81·127	4·148	18·028	2·074	
10 x 6	42	12·36	211·614	22·930	42·323	7·643	
12 x 6	44	12·95	315·439	22·257	52·573	7·419	

The cross sectional area of a joist and its weight per foot lineal have very little influence on its strength although at first sight one might think that a piece of steel which is double the weight of another piece is twice as strong.

The cross sectional area and weight of a steel joist (one is tied to the other) do of course have a certain amount of influence on the load bearing capacity, but they are by no means the governing factor.

The chief factor in the strength of a steel joist to resist flexure is not the weight or its area, but the disposition of the metal in the joist; putting the metal where it is most needed.

22·60 TONS

4·00 TONS

10" × 6" × 42 lbs. R.S.J PLACED FOR LONG AND SHORT AXIS

Fig. 94   Fig. 95

Take as an example the 10in. × 6in. × 42lb. R.S.J. Over a span of 10ft., placed as in Fig. 94, it will bear a distributed load of 22·60 tons, but placed as in Fig. 95 it will only support a distributed load of 4·00 tons approximately. It is exactly the same joist, same weight, load and span and yet there is such a vast difference in its bearing capacity.

What is a strong joist if used correctly becomes a death trap if placed in position without knowledge. The secret lies in its moment of inertia. Do not let the word "moment" worry you; it is merely an engineer's way of saying "amount"; the thing to worry about is "inertia".

Inertia baffled men of science for centuries, so we may be excused if in our turn we find ourselves a little dubious on the subject.

The word itself is difficult to explain. Every conceivable material possesses the quality of inertia—steel, copper, timber, orange peel, marzipan; the baffling part of it is that for two totally different materials of the same size and section, say a piece of timber and a piece of steel each 10in. deep by 4in. wide, the moment of inertia is identical, and yet we know that there is a vast difference in their strength.

Inertia is intangible. You cannot see it, touch it, taste it, smell it or feel it. If a steel joist is cut through with a hacksaw you will not find it or see it as you would the end grain of a piece of timber. It is not even like a gas, which although invisible may be smelt, or one can put a match to it and watch the resulting flame or explosion. It is not similar to weight, which although invisible and indefinable to the touch, makes itself felt if an effort, however slight, is made to lift an object.

The explanation of inertia is that it is a mathematical abstraction, an idea; real enough to a mathematician, but strange and incomprehensible to an ordinary mortal, a thing alien to everyday speech and the accepted meaning of words. There lies the whole difficulty.

The moment of inertia is the most important property of any beam, joist, lintel or bressummer in governing its strength to resist flexure whether the beam be made of steel, aluminium, or timber.

9" × 3" TIMBER
BEAM
FIG. 96

Proceeding step by step let us consider a timber beam say 9in. × 3in. as in Fig. 96. Now place a weight on top as in Fig. 97. If the weight is too much for the strength of the timber the beam would commence to bend and we should have the effect as shown in the diagram. Now increase the weight considerably as shown in Fig. 98 until the beam snaps.

It is obvious that on the top of the beam there is a considerable compression spread all over the fibres, while at the bottom of the beam the fibres have been completely pulled apart due to the extreme tension, so that in the one beam there is tension and compression.

It follows that compression must end somewhere and tension begin. Where these two opposing forces meet (for an indefinably thin layer) the effect of each must be zero. There must be a layer of fibres in the beam which remain entirely without compression or tension. This point is called the neutral axis and is obviously through the centre of the beam as in Fig. 99.

What we have to find out is in what way the known action of

placing a weight on a beam, thus causing compression and tension, may be counteracted, so that the beam does not fail.

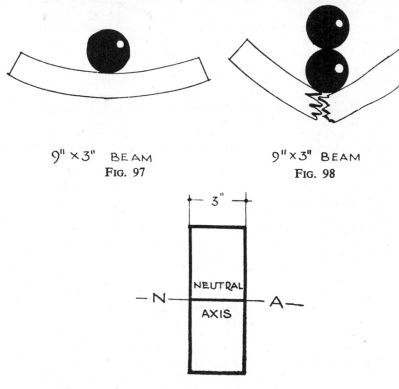

9" × 3" BEAM
FIG. 97

9" × 3" BEAM
FIG. 98

FIG. 99

The whole answer lies in the moment of inertia. (For the purposes of this chapter all secondary causes are ignored.)

That most wonderful scientist the world has ever known, Sir Isaac Newton, discovered (incidental to his stupendous work on mass, weight and gravitation) that the structural strength of a material depends not only on the kind of material but on its disposition, and further, that the ability to withstand strains and stresses depended on a certain physical phenomena which was called inertia, and that the exact amount or value or moment of the inertia could be calculated by a very intricate mathematical process. The trouble was that this mathematical process was so complicated that no one could accomplish it until Sir Isaac Newton with his great genius showed that this immense calculation could be carried out simply (at least simply to him). This reasoning he called his "Method of Fluxions" later called "The Infinitesimal Calculus", and later still divided into two parts called "The Differential and Integral Calculus".

Newton's work in this sphere of mathematics has never been superseded or even equalled: indeed, it forms the basis for all modern science where the use of mathematics is necessary, from the tilt of an aeroplane wing to a curve of error, from the expansion of a gas to the speed of a rocket.

It will be found that this is not as formidable as might at first appear.

The moment of inertia is equal to the sum of each elementary area multiplied by the square of its distance from the neutral axis. Fig. 100 makes this clear. It is an 8in. × 3in. beam chosen for convenience of calculation.

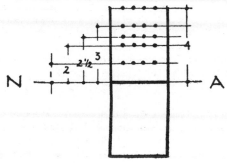

FIG. 100

The five rows of dots represent separate particles of the material very wide apart by comparison with the size of the beam. The dots on the topmost edge are obviously 4in. distant from the neutral axis, those on the second row are 3in., those on the third row are 2½in. and so on.

Let us single out one complete set of dots from top to bottom of the section. The distance squared from the first dot to the neutral axis is 16, that of the second down is 9, that of the third down is 6·25, the fourth is 4·00 and the fifth is 1·00. Regard the distance of each dot from the neutral axis as a little lever arm.

It follows that if the first dot (representing a particle of the material) will safely take a stress of 8 tons per sq. in. (the allowable safe working stress on structural steel) the second minute particle of material will only withstand a strain of nine sixteenths of 8 tons and so on in regular proportion to the distance of the dot from the neutral axis.

The allowable stress of 8 tons per sq. in. is whittled down considerably by reason of the fact that it is only the extreme fibres of a beam which can bear the full stress of 8 tons per sq. in. The allowable working stress declines rapidly in proportion to the square of the distance from the neutral axis, until, when it reaches the centre of the beam the stress allowed is nil.

But look again at the dots on the diagram. They are very wide apart and very coarse. Imagine the dots to be a million times smaller than shown in the diagram and to be a million times closer together; when you have got used to that idea imagine them to be a million times closer still, and that this vast infinite number of dots shall each have its area and value calculated by evaluating its square from the neutral axis. This is the problem Sir Isaac Newton resolved.

It is obvious from the beam in question that the real problem is to find the sum of all the squares between 4·00 and zero which spread over the cross sectional area of the beam gives the answer required.

Draw a graph as in Fig. 101 to any convenient scale, and along the x axis plot the numbers 0 to 4 inclusive. Along the y axis plot the squares of these numbers; horizontally there will be a length of 4 units whilst vertically there will be a length of 16 units.

If you have drawn the graph very accurately and count up the squares you will find that the area enclosed by the curve and the two axes is between 22 and 23 units. This area must contain all possible squares between 16 and zero.

The area enclosed on the graph is shown again in Fig. 102 but filled solid in black. The examples chosen have been selected at random. The square of 3·75 which is 14·06 and the square of 1·98 which is 3·92. It will be found that these results can be read from the y axis of the graph in proportion to the accuracy with which it is drawn.

If the black area were so covered with white lines of varying length equal to every possible square, the black would entirely disappear and the figure would become white when all possible squares had been drawn in.

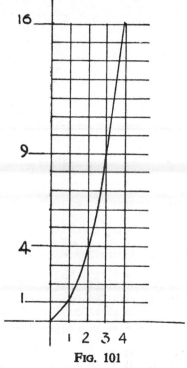

Fig. 101

So far our progress has been good, but it must be borne in mind that the calculation up to this stage depends on the accuracy with which we can draw graphs. If our eyesight is bad, or we are unskilful draughtsmen, or the instruments we use are crude or out of set, the resultant graph will be that much inaccurate and the calculation will be correspondingly in error.

Newton saw through to the heart of this problem and found a means of dispensing with the aid of graphs altogether. From an insuperable difficulty it had become soluble in a rough and ready manner by means of graphs, and from graphs it had become possible to obtain an answer to the highest pitch of accuracy by means of mathematics.

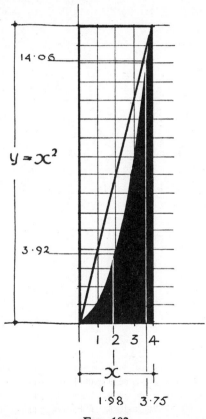

Fig. 102

A study of the graph shows that along the y axis are plotted all the squares of the numbers noted on the x axis; stated algebraically it is $y = x^2$; what we have to find is the extent of the area coloured black.

If we measured the whole of the area as shown in Fig. 102 it would obviously be x times y, but we already know that $y = x^2$, so that the whole area would be equal to x^3, that is, x times x^2. This area is obviously much too large. If we halved the area as shown by the strong black line in Fig. 102 we should have two equal triangles each equal to $\dfrac{x^3}{2}$, but as we can see this would still be too large.

Newton, by a piece of brilliant deductive reasoning which has never been equalled, found that the mathematically correct value for the area enclosed between the two ordinates of the diagram and the curve is in fact exactly $\dfrac{x^3}{3}$ and this holds good for all similar areas whatever the value of x might be.

For instance x might be equal to 2·50 in which case, when integrated, as a mathematician would say, the required answer would be $\dfrac{2{\cdot}50 \times 2{\cdot}50 \times 2{\cdot}50}{3}$ or x might be 13 when the answer would be $\dfrac{13 \times 13 \times 13.}{3}$

Notice how beautifully simple Newton made the whole operation. Simply add 1 to the index number of x^2 thus $x^{2+1} = x^3$ then divide the result by the new index number giving $\dfrac{x^3}{3}$.

Now let us look once more at the area as calculated by reading direct from the graph. I made the area equal to between 22 and 23 units.

The time has now come when we can dispense with the graph and try Newtons' method.

$$\frac{4 \times 4 \times 4}{3} = 21{\cdot}33$$ so that the result calculated from the graph was no far out.

An interesting sidelight on Newton and his wonderful method of fluxions may be mentioned here. A contemporary, Gottfried Wilhelm Leibniz, a German mathematician, discovered practically the same methods independently and unbeknown to Newton, which led to an involved controversy as to whom should belong the honour and prestige of prior discovery.

Books on mechanics generally give the formula for finding the moment of inertia of a beam as follows: — $\frac{bd^3}{12}$ which seems very remote from what we have been doing. The two, however, are one and the same thing which can easily be shown. The drawback of a formula such as this is that many people use it without really knowing what it means with consequent uncertainty in their work.

Examine the graph as shown in Fig. 101 once more and it will be noted that the units along the x axis are really half the depth of the beam. In a beam 8in. deep, half the depth is 4in. and it is this length which is ticked off along the x axis.

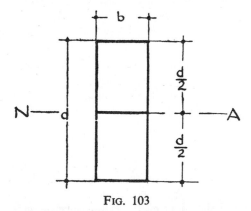

Fig. 103

If we do not wish to take any particular numerical example

we can use letters instead which can be applied to any sized beam we like to name. Instead of saying that a beam is 4in. wide by 8in. deep we can say (for convenience) that it is b in. wide by d in. deep as in Fig. 103.

Half the depth of the beam measured from the top to the neutral axis is obviously d divided by 2 which is $\dfrac{d}{2}$ but $\dfrac{d}{2}$ is exactly the same as x which when integrated as already shown becomes $\dfrac{x^3}{3}$ so we arrive at the following expression:

$$\frac{d \times d \times d}{2 \times 2 \times 2 \times 3} = \frac{d^3}{24}$$

Multiply this result by b, the breadth of the beam, and again by 2 (for the top and bottom halves) and we obtain the expression:

$$\frac{d^3 \times b \times 2}{24} = \frac{bd^3}{12}.$$

Chapter XI

STANCHIONS

A STEEL stanchion is one of the most ingenious methods of building construction ever devised. It not only makes use of the economic value of steel to its fullest extent, but by its use it enables vast loads to be safely supported within the minimum space and ground area.

A stanchion makes it possible to carry a load of 60 tons within the width of a 9in. wall, to support a load of 160 tons within less than the breadth of a man's shoulders; to place tremendous burdens where otherwise the supports would collapse through inadequate strength.

Of all the factors involved in steelwork design, stanchions are the most difficult to calculate both as regards their physical and mathematical properties. The mathematical and physical behaviour of steel stanchions have been under investigation for many years.

Despite the vast amount of research carried out by engineers and mathematicians it is still impossible to account for the behaviour of stanchions under the various forms of concentric and eccentric loading; the difficulties are so great in fact that even the most experienced engineers have not been able to resolve the problem in an entirely satisfactory manner, and can do no more than arrive at conclusions which they have been bound to name "Empirical Formulæ"; in so many words mathematical formulæ which have been arrived at by "trial and error" which will fit the observed facts as near as possible.

It is a well-known fact that if a piece of timber (say 3ft. 0in. × 4in. × 3in.) has a cap and base fixed to it and is then secured truly vertical, it will bear a reasonable load, placed concentrically, without signs of deflection, as illustrated in Fig. 104.

Now take exactly the same scantling as before, namely 4in. × 3in., but this time use a length of 18ft. 0in. and erect in position with exactly the same load as before as in Fig. 105.

The difference is amazing. The cross sectional area of the

strut is the same as in the first example, 12 sq. in., yet the strut is swaying about and bending as though it were under a heavy load; in fact the column would sway about if the load were removed.

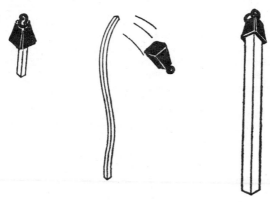

Figs. 104, 105, 106

What causes the whipping and bending of the strut and at what point in the height of the column will the bending and curvature commence?

Should the cross sectional area of the column be increased, a load equal in weight to the previous example could quite easily be supported at a height of 18ft. 0in. as in Fig. 106.

The next question is obviously, "By what proportion must the cross sectional area be increased to carry a stated concentric load for any height named?"

These two great questions (which govern the whole of stanchion design) can only be satisfactorily answered up to a point, the rest of the design relying on nothing more nor less than trained trial and error.

It is now apparent that the strength of a column depends on the ratio between the cross sectional area at the base and the height of the column itself, which in its turn indicates an infinite variation in allowable working stress for the condition of supporting a concentric load.

It is important to stress here, that so far the discussion has

L

dealt only with concentric loading, that is where the central point of the system of loading brings the whole of its weight to bear over the exact centre of the stanchion. Eccentric loading has its own troubles and complications which will be investigated later.

It must be noted, that in practice, the perfect theoretical system of concentric loading is difficult to realise. There is always some slight eccentricity which must be allowed for in computation.

It is this question of change in permissible working stress for variation in height which causes the whole complication in stanchion design. The early investigators thought they had mastered this important point when they tried to assess change in allowable stress according to the ratio obtained from a comparison of the height of a column with its diameter. This comparison gave good results within certain small limits, and then unexpectedly failed for no apparent reason.

When a theory is only right "so far" it is time to discard it and search for something more in accordance with the facts. Such a theory, after innumerable tests, was found, and also the reason why the first theory failed.

The allowable safe working stress on a steel column, of whatever section (H, angle, channel, or circular) depends on the ratio of its radius of gyration to its height; each dimension being expressed in inches.

The ratio of the diameter of a circular column, or if square of its axis or diagonals, to the height, was proved to have little or no influence on the alteration in stress.

Before much further headway can be made in understanding the action of columns under stress, the term radius of gyration must be defined and thoroughly mastered.

Again it is a question of a mathematical abstraction, like that of the moment of inertia with which it is closely bound.

The engineers investigating the strength of stanchions had already satisfied themselves that a given load produced increasing instability and flexure as the height increased, and deduced from this the fact that the allowable stress in the section must be correspondingly decreased, but in what proportions and by how much?

It was found in fact that if the (this is going to be difficult) cross sectional area of a stanchion could be considered as wobbling round and round the two axes of the section, the stanchion would be structurally sound, provided the stress was equated to the moment of inertia, and that this value, or the radius of the gyrating action (hence the name radius of gyration) was divided into the height of the stanchion.

This is an example of an empirical formula.

The measurement of the radius of gyration is a lineal measurement expressed in inches and is equal to the perpendicular distance from the respective axis of a stanchion to such a point, that if the whole cross section area were there concentrated, the moment of inertia would not be altered in any way.

We have already seen how the moment of inertia is the chief property for determining the strength of a beam.

Place the beam on end and use it as a column and the same conditions regarding the moment of inertia still hold good, but qualified as we shall see by the radius of gyration.

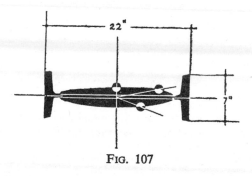

Fig. 107

Fig. 107 shows a 22in. × 7in. × 75lb. R.S.J. used as a stanchion. The cross sectional area is 22·00in. with a maximum moment of inertia of 1676·796 whilst the minimum moment of inertia is only 41·065.

Notice the vast difference between the moments of inertia for one and the same beam or stanchion. This emphasises the important point in the calculation of this property. The maximum moment is comprised of the sum of all possible squares between 11 and zero, whilst in the case of the minimum moment we have all possible squares between 3·50 and zero.

The next step in determining the radius of gyration is that this value or property resolves, not in a circle, but in an ellipse according as to whether the inertia is calculated for the long or short axis of the steelwork section. (In steelwork tables these are always denoted as the X and Y axes respectively.)

Fig. 107 shows the ellipse of gyration.

The radii are 1·36 and 8·71.

Taking the least radius of gyration first (which governs the weakest condition of the pillar) we have to find out how this quantity is related to the moment of inertia, in such a way, that if the cross sectional area of the section were concentrated at this particular spot on the circumference of the ellipse, the moment of inertia would remain the same.

The dot (purely diagrammatic) shown revolving in Fig. 107 represents this action as though it were the path of a planet; the area is constant, whilst the moment of inertia and the radius of gyration each vary in exact proportion with each other as the dot sways round the axis.

Bearing in mind the definition of the moment of inertia, the whole area of the section can be regarded as acting through its centre of gravity and the radius of gyration squared, when multiplied by the cross sectional area should equal the moment of inertia.

This reasoning will become clearer if we take an actual numerical example and check the results by the published steelwork tables. The results given will differ very slightly from the printed tables on account of the four figure logarithm tables used and other small differences.

(It is not essential to use logarithm tables if you wish to work direct, but the computation will be much more laborious.)

$$22\text{in.} \times 7\text{in.} \times 75\text{lb. R.S.J.}$$

Cross sectional area 22·064.

Maximum moment of inertia 1676·796.

Maximum radius of gyration 8·718.

Area x maximum radius of gyration squared = maximum moment of inertia.

$$22\text{·}064 \times (8\text{·}718)^2$$

log   0·9404

        2
        ———

$$\begin{array}{ll} & 1\cdot8808 \\ \log & 1\cdot3438 \\ \hline & 3\cdot2246 \qquad \text{Anti log} = 1677\cdot00 \end{array}$$

PUBLISHED MAXIMUM MOMENT 1676·796

Minimum moment of inertia 41·065.
Minimum radius of gyration 1·364.
22·064 x (1·364)^2

$$\begin{array}{ll} \log & 0\cdot1348 \\ & \quad\,\,\, 2 \\ \hline & 0\cdot2696 \\ \log & 1\cdot3438 \\ \hline & 1\cdot6134 \qquad \text{Anti log} = 41\cdot060. \end{array}$$

PUBLISHED MINIMUM MOMENT 41·065

The above examples carried out in extenso for both moments of inertia prove the proposition.

In mathematical language and as given in the textbooks the radius of gyration is designated by the letter g.

Its value is generally set out in the following formula:—

$$g = \sqrt{\dfrac{I}{A}}$$

I = moment of inertia.

A = area of section.

Test the examples which we have already proved.

$$g = \sqrt{\dfrac{1676\cdot796}{22\cdot064}} = \log \begin{array}{l} 3\cdot2246 \\ 1\cdot3438 \end{array}$$

$$2 \,\, \sqrt{\,\, 1\cdot8808}$$

$$\cdot9404$$

Anti log   ·9404 = 8·718

$$g = \sqrt{\frac{41\cdot065}{22\cdot064}} = \log \quad \begin{array}{r} 1\cdot6135 \\ 1\cdot3438 \\ \hline \end{array}$$

$$2 \ \sqrt{\quad \cdot2697}$$

$$\cdot1354$$

$$\text{Anti log} \quad \cdot1354 = 1\cdot365$$

It would be fruitless to check compound stanchions from the tables by the same method because of the fact that deductions for rivet holes in each flange have to be taken into consideration.

These calculations are very laborious and in no way add to our knowledge or understanding of the radius of gyration.

A rough check can of course be made when it will be found that the results obtained are larger in value than those in the printed tables; the tables being calculated on the net value after full deduction for rivet holes.

The permissible stress on a column is variable in direct proportion to the ratio which exists between the radius of gyration and the height of the column, both expressed in inches.

For beams the allowable safe working stress is 8 tons per sq. in. of cross sectional area (or 10 tons if we like to work to the 1948 tables). Note in the above the decline in the factor of safety.

Whatever the position of the beam, whatever its method of loading, whatever the bending moment, span or method of fixing, the working stress remains the same: *Not so for stanchions*. The higher the stanchion in comparison with its radius of gyration, the smaller the allowable working stress.

I am sorry to have to tell you that there is a further complication. Stanchions (apart from all other difficulties in their design and computation) are known by the methods used in their fixing both from the practical and theoretical standpoint.

The following are the terms used by engineers to decide what value of stress shall be used:—

1. Both ends round.
2. Both ends fixed.

3. Both ends flat.
4. Both ends hinged.
5. One end hinged, one end fixed.
6. Both ends fixed. (L.C.C.)

Numbers 4, 5 and 6 are terms used in the London Building Acts, generally known as L.C.C. formula, whilst the first three are known as the Moncrieff formula. "Both ends fixed" in the L.C.C. formula has a different signification to the Moncrieff formula.

These six classifications were an attempt to define all possible methods of securing the base and head of a stanchion; the method of fixing having a great influence on its stability and hence in determining what value of stress should be used in the calculations, and as indicated by the ratio of slenderness.

The ratio of slenderness is the term given to the quotient obtained by dividing the height of the column by the least radius of gyration; its algebraical expression is 1.

It is important to note that it is the *least* radius which is used. This covers the worst possible case which is likely to occur in stanchion design.

The British Standards Institution made a valiant effort to simplify stanchion design in the revised tables 1948: B.S. 449.

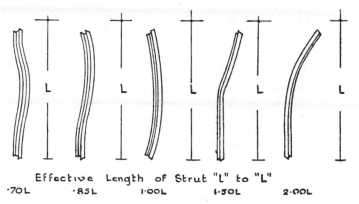

Effective Length of Strut "L" to "L"

·70L   ·85L   1·00L   1·50L   2·00L

FIG. 108

They cancelled the six conditions of fixing already described and substituted five main conditions as shown in the table below and as indicated in Fig. 108.

Type	Effective length of strut 1
1. Effectively held in position and restrained in direction at both ends	·7L
2. Effectively held in position at both ends and restrained in direction at one end	·85L
3. Effectively held in position at both ends but not restrained in direction	L
4. Effectively held in position and restrained in direction at one end and at the other end partially restrained in direction but not held in position	1·5L
5. Effectively held in position and restrained in direction at one end but not held in position restrained in direction at the other end ..	2·00L

The decrease in stress is obtained not only by making use of the ratio of slenderness but by the use of the hitherto unknown property, effective length.

Effective length is not the true height of the stanchion, but is its conventional height arrived at by the use of an empirical formula, and is not confined solely to mathematical reasoning.

An examination of the tables for stanchions concentrically loaded by the Moncrieff formula, the L.C.C. formula and the latest 1948/1949 formula, leaves one in the utmost confusion. There is hardly a point of agreement between them as the following comparison shows; a few sections being selected at random.

All the tables, however, have one thing in common. They show how the stress varies according to the ratio of slenderness.

The first two tables are calculated for a stress of 8 tons per sq. in., while the last and latest table is worked on a basis of 9 tons per sq. in.

As is to be expected, there is a 12½ per cent. increase in the value of the concentric load which may be carried for certain sections and heights, but in other cases the loads which may be safely carried are totally unrelated to each other. This reflects the difficulty of stanchion design and the fact that opinion largely enters into it.

TABLE 3.	CONCENTRIC LOADS — MONCRIEFF FORMULA						
STANCHION			HEIGHTS IN FEET			(ENDS FLAT)	
	3	4	5	6	7	8	9	10
9in. x 7in. x 50	97·60	97·00	96·20	95·20	94·00	92·60	91·00	89·20
9in. x 4in. x 21	39·90	38·80	37·40	35·70	33·70	27·50	21·70	17·60
8in. x 6in. x 35	68·10	67·40	66·60	65·60	64·40	63·00	61·40	59·60

TABLE 4.	CONCENTRIC LOADS — L.C.C. FORMULA						
STANCHION			HEIGHTS IN FEET			(ENDS FIXED)	
	3	4	5	6	7	8	9	10
9in. x 7in. x 50	87·60	84·90	82·20	79·60	76·90	74·20	71·50	68·90
9in. x 4in. x 21	33·30	31·10	28·80	26·50	24·30	22·00	19·80	17·50
8in. x 6in. x 35	60·20	57·90	55·70	53·40	51·20	48·90	46·70	44·50

TABLE 5.	CONCENTRIC LOADS — 1948/449						
STANCHION			HEIGHTS IN FEET				
	3	4	5	6	7	8	9	10
9in. x 7in. x 50	116·00	111·00	106·00	101·00	96·00	90·80	85·60	80·40
9in. x 4in. x 21	42·40	38·00	33·60	29·20	24·80	20·80	17·50	14·80
8in. x 6in. x 35	79·60	75·30	70·90	66·60	62·20	57·90	53·50	49·10

In the welter of confusing tables, formulæ, stress values and ratios of slenderness, what is the average builder to do on a small job? He is not a structural engineer or a mathematician; all he wants to do is to get on with the job and put in a couple of stanchions to carry a concentric load, and to feel reasonably certain that his work is safe.

Now that he understands the use and construction of the tables he can make his choice of a suitable stanchion. For this purpose I suggest the use of the L.C.C. formula, but at the same time it must not be forgotten that the revised by-laws may be insisted on to the letter, in which case there is no alternative but to conform to CP/113 or BS 449. A word or two in time with the local surveyor to the authority will settle this before going to too much trouble.

Before further progress can be made it is necessary to append here a table of ratios of slenderness BS 449. It is to be noted that the term "axial load" is substituted for "concentric load".

l = effective length and not actual length.
r = radius of gyration.

PERMISSIBLE WORKING STRESSES IN TONS PER SQUARE INCH
OF CROSS SECTION FOR AXIAL LOADS

l/r	Stress in tons inch^2
0	9·00
10	8·51
20	8·03
30	**7·54**
40	7·06
50	6·57
60	6·09
70	5·60
80	5·12
90	4·62
100	**4·13**
110	3·67

A few examples may be shown. A stanchion is required to carry a concentric load of 19 tons at a height of 10ft. above floor level.

Refer to B.S. 449 tables. Look along the top of the column for height in feet until you come to 10 and down until you come to 19 tons or nearest above this load. There is the choice of 10in. × 4½in. × 25lb., which will carry 21·80 tons at a height of 10ft., or a 5in. × 4½in. × 20lb., which will carry 20·70 tons.

Unfortunately, neither of these sections will do; there is something else to take into consideration: the depth of the stanchion below floor level, say, a further 2ft., making the total height 12ft.

The choice now rests between a 10in. × 5in. × 30lb., or a 6in. × 5in. × 25lb., which stanchions will carry a concentric load of 23·50 tons and 21·30 tons respectively.

In the next example it is required to carry a concentric load of 95 tons on a stanchion, of which the actual height is · 10ft. Following the same method as before we find that there are several joists which will meet the case, but they all seem rather unwieldy in section.

A 22in. × 7in. × 75lb. will carry 103 tons, and 18in. × 7in. × 75lb. will carry 110 tons (this section is more convenient as regards dimensions, and is no heavier than the first section, although it will carry a heavier load) and finally there is a 12in. × 8in. × 65lb. which will support a load of 111 tons; and this is the stanchion I should choose.

It will now be useful to check the examples by means of the ratio of slenderness and the permissible stress.

STANCHION 12FT. HIGH

Section 10in. × 5in. × 30lb.

Area 8·85 sq. in.

Least radius of gyration 1·05.

Ratio of slenderness — $\dfrac{12 \times 12}{1·05} = 138$

Allowable stress for ratio of slenderness of 138 = 2·65 tons per sq. in.

Safe concentric load = 2·65 × 8·85 = 23·45 tons.

STANCHION 10FT. HIGH

Section 12in. × 8in. × 65lb.

Area 19·12 sq. in.

Least radius of gyration 1·85.

Ratio of slenderness = $\dfrac{10 \times 12}{1·85} = 65$

Allowable stress for ratio of slenderness of 65 = 5·85 tons per sq. in.

Safe concentric load = 5·85 × 19·12 = 111·85 tons.

The calculations dealt with so far have been where the loading has been concentrically placed. Where the loading is eccentrically placed further complications ensue.

In practice stanchions are very often eccentrically loaded due to many things, possibly the space available for the placing of the column, or picking up a load from an awkwardly placed R.S.J., or brackets have to be used in order to accommodate the end of several beams.

Let us assume that the load of 19 tons in our last example was carried by the flange of the stanchion with a bracket under as in Fig. 109.

Although the load is exactly the same as in the previous example, we shall find that our 10in. × 5in. stanchion is now (due to the condition of loading) of no use.

There is still the effect of a concentric load, in so far as both flanges and the web together bear their share of resisting flexure, and also the central axis of the pillar still represents the neutral axis.

The load itself may be considered as having travelled along the beam to its very end when it immediately transfers itself to the stanchion with a bending effort equal in lever arm to the distance from the neutral axis to the outside edge of the flange as shown in Fig. 109.

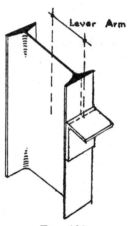

FIG. 109

The Code of Practice 113 requires that the full extent of the lever arm in a case like this shall be carried to the extreme edge of the angle plate; for ease of calculation let us take this as 1in., although in practice it might be no more than ¾in. or ½in.

Suppose we try the following working: —

Stanchion 16in. × 6in. × 62lb.

Area 18·21 sq. in.

Section modulus 90·63.

Lever arm for eccentric loading 8in. + 1in. = 9in.

Bending moment in inch tons due to eccentric loading
= 19 × 9 = 171 in. tons.

$$\text{Added stress due to eccentric loading} = \frac{171}{90 \cdot 63} = 1 \cdot 80$$

(round figures).

Equivalent concentric load $= 19 \cdot 00 + (1 \cdot 80 \times 18 \cdot 21)$
$= 32 \cdot 78 + 19 \cdot 00 = 51 \cdot 79$ tons.

Tabular load carried $= 60 \cdot 70$ tons.

It is to be noted that other sections, say, an 18in. × 6in. × 55lb. which would carry a load of $53 \cdot 30$ tons at a height of 12ft., might prove unsatisfactory by reason of the fact that the cross sectional area is less than the section we have chosen whilst the lever arm would be 2in. longer; this type of calculation depends a lot on practice in selection.

Caps, baseplates and brackets are more or less standard for each type of stanchion.

The main thing to remember in eccentric loading of pillars is that to the effect of weight is added the incidence of leverage giving tremendous power to the forces tending to buckle or cause flexure to the pillar.

The aim then is to reduce this new force to the equivalent of a concentrically placed load.

Often a nice point is arrived at in design, whether to connect the beam direct to the web of the stanchion, thus considerably reducing the lever arm, but limiting oneself to the weaker way of the section, or to connect the beam to the flange, taking advantage of the stronger way of the section but greatly increasing the lever arm.

The ready answer to such questions as this can only come with experience.

Chapter XII

BENDING MOMENTS

A BENDING moment is the measure of the forces acting on a beam which tend to induce bending or flexure in the material of which the beam is composed. It is in no wise dependent on the material of which a beam is constructed, or the method of construction of the beam, or its manner of fixing.

For a given span and a given load the bending moment is exactly the same whether the joist is composed of steel, reinforced concrete or timber.

Bending moments from their very nature are always compound measurements; foot tons, inch tons, foot pounds, or inch pounds, whichever is the most convenient for the calculation in hand.

To understand fully what is the nature of bending moments as they affect beams we must first of all know what is meant by reaction and equilibrium. The general laws of mechanics state that for every action there must be an equal and opposite reaction for a body to remain in equilibrium. Rest your hand lightly on the wall and you will be hardly aware that you are doing so; push heavily and you will hurt your wrist; clench your fist and let go a pile-driver, you will smash your hand.

That is action and reaction! When you press on the wall with a force equal to the fraction of an ounce the wall gives back a pressure of a fraction of an ounce; smash into the wall with a force of 90lb., the wall reciprocates. Had the wall been built to withstand no more than a force of 80lb., it would have crumbled under the impact of a force of 90lb.

There is this physical peculiarity to notice. A structure or support of any kind can only give a reaction up to the limit of the stress of which it is capable, but cannot of itself produce a force or pressure beyond the action put upon it.

Thus, a dam wall built in masonry in which each stone weighs several hundredweights and is keyed into its neighbour is capable of resisting a terrific pressure per square foot. Apply a pressure of a few ounces and the reaction is a few ounces; the wall (despite its tremendous strength) cannot hit back, or shoot you into the air, or push you over.

On the other hand, let flood water come, exerting a vast pressure against the masonry which exceeds the limit of reaction for which the wall was designed: we all know the result.

Action and reaction are difficult things to grasp because there is no apparent movement; we cannot actually see a support pushing and pulling, thrusting or strutting itself against the stress of a load. The whole action is static.

It is the unseen action or tendency to action which is the first essential in calculating a bending moment. What we are really calculating is the tendency of the weight transmitted to a support to push against and bend up the girder held down by the load placed thereon. Fig. 110 makes this clear.

If the hand were placed just underneath the load no weight would be experienced. Place the hand underneath the other end and the fingers would be squashed. The explanation is that the effect of the load (designated in mechanics, W) has travelled along the beam until it is transferred to the pier, which in turn transfers the pressure to the ground.

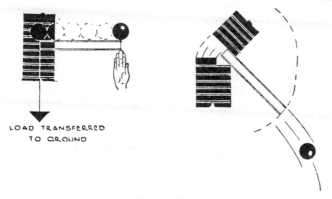

LOAD TRANSFERRED
TO GROUND

Figs. 110, 111

The reaction of the pier must be equal to the combined weight of the load W, the weight of the beam, and the weight of the pier or wall above the tail of the girder.

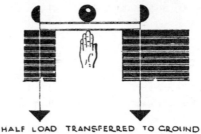

HALF LOAD TRANSFERRED TO GROUND

FIG. 112

If the tail load were inadequate we should have the result shown in Fig. 111. Fig. 112 shows the same weight placed centrally on a joist. The reaction in this case is $\dfrac{W}{2}$. The weight travels along the fibres of the beam equally in all directions until it meets the supports. The fact that one pier happens to be twice as large as the other has no effect on the equality of the end reactions.

If it were possible for the reaction at the left hand pier to be more than $\dfrac{W}{2}$ we should have the effect shown in Fig. 113.

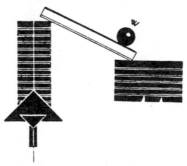

Upward Action on Pier
greater than Half W

FIG. 113

Our attention must now be transferred to leverage. All bending moments, for whatever system of girders used, and whatever the disposition of the loading, are nothing more nor less than computations of leverage. The leverage in a beam or girder is rather difficult to imagine, because once again the whole structure is static; there are no movable parts, wheels or pistons as in mechanical engineering, but the leverage is there nevertheless.

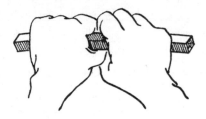

FIG. 114

If we take a small piece of oak, say 1½in. square by 10in. long, and grip it with both hands close together as in Fig. 114, we shall experience the utmost difficulty in breaking it; but take the same section 4ft. long and we can break it with ease.

The importance of this experiment is that in the first instance we exerted all our strength and were unable to fracture a small section of oak; in the second example we only put forth a *small* amount of effort, yet we could break the section with ease. That is leverage.

The physical phenomenon of leverage was one of the earliest effects to be studied by mathematicians and philosophers who enunciated clear and simple laws for the admeasurement of load, placing, pressure, and length of lever arm to help man overcome by mechanical means what his puny strength could not accomplish itself.

Whereas in mechanical engineering levers are calculated in order to find out the necessary data for lifting or moving weights, in girder construction we do just the opposite. We calculate the leverage to find out how to *keep* the load from moving.

Fig. 115 shows a typical case of leverage, where a very heavy load W, on a short lever arm may be easily lifted by the application of a comparatively light pressure applied to a long lever arm. The components of leverage are compound as we have already stated when referring to bending moments.

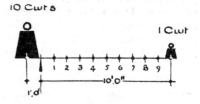

FIG. 115

Thus, in the above example, if we translate it into numerical quantities, the leverage from the fulcrum to the centre of gravity of the superimposed weight is 10ft. cwt., that is, 10cwt. times a distance of 1ft. To balance it on the right hand side of the fulcrum we have 10ft. times 1 cwt. = 10ft. cwt.

Any pressure or weight over the amount of 1cwt., even the fraction of an ounce, will enable the load of 10cwt. to be manipulated with ease, either in an upward or downward direction. Fig. 116 shows what happens when the crowbar used to prise up a heavy stone breaks. The illustration shows the effect of a bending moment.

FIG. 116

The leverage induced by the placing of a load in various positions and the length of the lever arm to balance or move the load is only incidental to the problem of designing a girder. We have to measure the exact mathematical and physical load which will just fracture the crowbar. Knowing this quantity, we can then multiply the strength of the crowbar as many times as we like consistent with our ideas of safety.

Bending moments for beams are generally dealt with by means of bending moment diagrams or formulæ, two very useful methods for quick working, but both methods have the same fault, in that they obscure the reasoning.

If, however, we can work from the known facts of reaction and leverage, the whole question of bending moments becomes clear and easily grasped. No system of loading or disposition of girders will be able to defy our efforts at solving.

The first and easiest bending moment to understand is that of the cantilever aready depicted in Fig. 110. It is obvious, even to the uninitiated, where the bending moment occurs, namely, at the point of support. If the beam is going to collapse under the superimposed load it will do so after the manner shown in Fig. 117. It is hardly likely that a little piece will break off from the end of the beam as shown in Fig. 118.

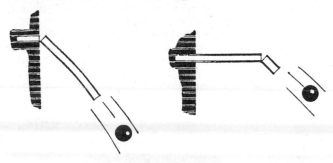

FIGS. 117, 118

Denote the load as W and the length of the lever arm as L. The resultant bending moment is WL ft. tons. A numerical example for a cantilever of 10ft. and a concentrated load at the end of the beam of 10 tons would be worked as follows:

10 tons × 10ft. = 100ft. tons.

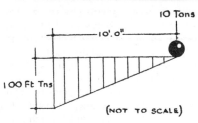

FIG. 119

A useful demonstration (to be resorted to only as a graphical check on the working) is to draw out the bending moment to scale as in Fig. 119 where the vertical line represents 100ft. tons, the resultant figure being a triangle.

A useful scale would be $\frac{1}{2}$in. = 25ft. tons, which would make one side of the triangle 2in. long. The length of the beam to the same scale would therefore be 5in. long. By filling in the triangle with ordinates for as close together as we choose, any corresponding bending moment may be read off to scale.

This is an exercise which is often given in books on graphic statics and manuals of steelwork construction. While it shows the diminution of the bending moment at any particular point of the beam, there is little other use for it.

The strength of any beam is invariably governed by its maximum bending moment, the minimum or intermediate bending moments being of no use for that special beam or its manner of loading. Fig. 120 shows the same cantilever, but this time with a uniformly distributed load of 10 tons.

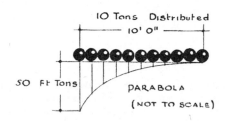

FIG. 120

The reaction at the pier is still 10 tons, since the load has nowhere else to go, but the bending moment is only *half* the value of the previous example, namely, 50ft. tons.

To arrive at this result the distributed load is taken as acting through its centre of gravity, or at half the length of the span. The working is therefore as follows:

$$10 \text{ tons} \times \frac{10\text{ft.}}{2} \text{ (half span)} = 50 \text{ ft. tons.}$$

The formula for a uniformly loaded cantilever is given in the textbooks as $\dfrac{wl^2}{2}$. The small w represents the superimposed load per foot run. For the complete span of 1ft. there is thus a full load of wl.

The bending moment is $wl \times \dfrac{1}{2} = \dfrac{wl^2}{2}$

If we wish to draw out the bending moment diagram it would turn out to be a parabola and each ordinate would be equal to $\dfrac{wl^2}{2}$.

It is useful to know how to construct a parabola quickly and accurately to scale. There are two methods to learn; one for a fairly deep and large parabola and the other for a shallow curve. The first method is to draw a rectangle with the base equal to the span of the curve and head equal to greatest rise of parabola as in Fig. 121.

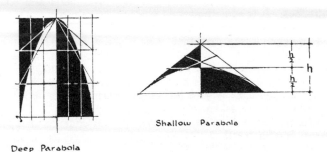

Deep Parabola

Shallow Parabola

FIGS. 121, 122

Divide the diagram into a suitable number of equal parts vertically and laterally, mark the crossings and draw tangents. It is now an easy matter to draw the curve through. Where the parabola is very flat it will be found more convenient to draw a triangle equal to twice the height of the required curve as in Fig. 122, divide the sides into equal parts, and draw tangents as before.

The parabola is one of the most important and oft recurring curves in mathematics. In the case of the uniformly loaded cantilever we are discussing, each ordinate of the parabola will be found to be equal to $\dfrac{wl^2}{2}$ and will give the corresponding bending moment at any point of the cantilever.

Cantilever construction is of the highest importance. Spandril ended steps as used in ornamental staircases depend for their elegance and strength on the fact that they are built into the wall at one end with sufficient weight imposed to counteract the maximum bending moment which could be induced by the steps being fully loaded with people right up to the spandril end.

Another example of cantilever is the standard steel bracket for connecting the ends of R.S.J.s to stanchions. Although the cantilever arm seldom exceeds 4in., it has tremendous leverage effect on the stanchion, according as to whether it is bolted to the flange or the web.

A familiar form of cantilever construction in common use is that of the marquise or canopy as used over hotel and cinema entrances. It is something which a builder is often called upon to construct in a simplified form.

The huge cinema marquise, weighing anything from 20 to 50 tons, is always the subject of specialist design, but the principles are fundamentally the same for a small canopy such as might be constructed over the entrance to a grain store, milking shed, shop warehouse, or any of the smaller requirements upon which a builder may be asked to give a design and price.

This particular type of cantilever (which contains many surprises) is well worth following out in detail, so let us take an example as shown in Fig. 123.

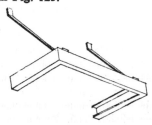

Fig. 123

Assume that a grocer wants you to erect a canopy over the entrance to his warehouse so that his goods can be unloaded in wet weather. The canopy extends over the loading bay for a distance of 5ft. and is to be 10ft. long. It is constructed out of light channel sections welded together at the angles, the top is covered with lead sheathed patent glazing and wired cast glass, an ornamental fascia is screwed to the sides and front of the canopy, and finally it is strapped back to the wall with two smith-made wrought iron twisted straps set at an angle of 45 degrees.

It must not be forgotten that what we are discussing is bending moments and not actual points in design of canopies or the attendant work which will arise in other trades.

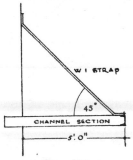

Fig. 124

Let us assume that the canopy weighs two tons. In diagrammatic form it will appear as in Fig. 124. We now come to the surprises! The introduction of the straps takes away the true cantilever principles of the construction.

Had the straps been omitted we should have had nothing but a simple cantilever to contend with. Let us do away with the straps, then! Too late! The customer has already seen them and wants them.

In a simple cantilever (as we have already seen) the whole of the supported weight ultimately rests on the wall. The same result applies here, but the interplay of the forces is totally different.

What we have landed ourselves with is a hybrid consisting of part cantilever, part simply supported beam, and part frame construction. (This latter is again only an approximate description; the canopy is by no means a true frame as an engineer would understand it.)

The true frame must consist of a triangle or series of triangles adequately bolted or riveted together as in Fig. 125, so that all forces acting upon it produce stresses in the three members which equalise. If they do not we have the result shown in Fig. 126, causing one or more members to part company.

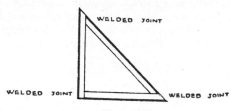

FIG. 125

If the shearing strength of the rivets or bolts is adequate and the bearing value of the metal sufficient, it is obvious that the ony means of deflecting the frame or causing its collapse is by the parting of the metal in the members. This is where the strength of a framed structure lies.

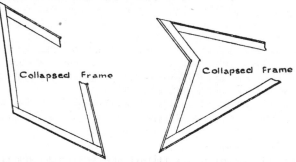

FIG. 126

You will notice that all trussed railway bridges, roof trusses, and trussed purlins are built on this principle. The most notable exception being the queen post roof truss, which is not a true frame, yet nevertheless very strong.

Now let us consider the best way to tackle the canopy. It weighs two tons evenly distributed over the whole of the frame. It is supported on the wall by the side channels where they enter the brickwork so that it does not take much deduction to decide that each channel supports a load of one ton. (In this demonstration it is intended to include the self weight of all structural work in the two tons.)

The patent glazing bears direct on to the front channel which is 10ft. span, all weight being transmitted by this member to the side channels.

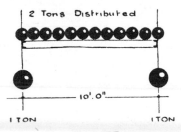

Fig. 127

Fig. 127 shows the front channel uniformly loaded. In ordinary circumstances the following would be the working for the end channels:

Cantilever span 5ft.

Concentrated load at end of span 1 ton.

Maximum bending moment 1 ton × 5ft. = 5ft. tons.

But the straps intervene, thus doing away with the free end and so altering the character of the forces, turning it almost (but not quite) into a framed structure as in Fig. 128. The 5ft. cantilever has in effect been turned into a beam supported at both ends.

Had the strap been vertical as in Fig. 129, there would have been no load on the cantilever beyond its own weight, and consequently no reaction at the wall end. The vertical tie would be supporting the whole load, and the metal would therefore be subject to a stress of 20cwt. spread over the cross sectional area of the rod.

Assuming a safe working stress of 5 tons per sq. in. for wrought iron, the section required would be ·20.², say, a ⅞ diameter rod. The side arm of the canopy would become unnecessary.

The strap, however, holds one end of the canopy just as though it were supported on a pier, except that the rod is fixed at an angle of 45 degrees to the channel iron, resulting in half the load being transferred along the 5ft. span channel and half being transferred direct to the brick wall above by means of the pull on the rod.

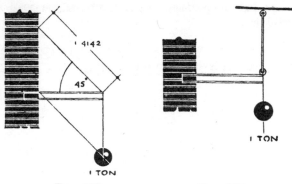

FIG. 128   FIG. 129

Referring again to Fig. 128, it is seen that the value of the stress in the strap must be pro rata to its inclination to its horizontal. By completing the parallelogram of forces we obtain the following equation:

$$\frac{20 \text{ cwt.}}{2} \times \cot 45 \text{ deg.} = \text{stress in tie bar}$$

$$= 10·00\text{cwt.} \times 1·4142 = 14·20\text{cwt.}$$

It must be noted there is no question of bending moment in this, but only of stress or pulling induced by the weight suspended at the end of the inclined strap.

We must also remember that we are not dealing with a true frame. There is no third steel member joining the brickwork end of the strap to the brickwork end of the channel. The problem may therefore be considered in another way.

The whole weight of 1 ton may be assumed to come on to the inclined strap, the side channel being treated merely as a sort of distance piece to keep the end of the strap at a distance of 5ft. from the wall.

The next problem to consider is that of a beam freely supported at both ends with a centrally placed load as in Fig. 130(1).

It is rather difficult at first sight to see where the effect of leverage comes in, in fact there does not appear to be any until we go back to the area of reaction, when it can immediately be grasped that each pier bears half the load pushing upwards against the fulcrum situated at the centre of the load as in Fig. 130(2).

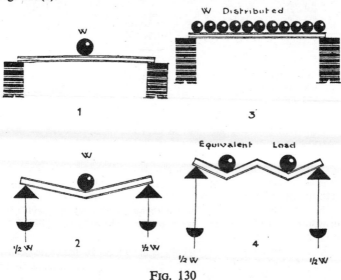

FIG. 130

The bending moment is now easily calculated:—

$$\frac{W}{2} \times \frac{L}{2} = \frac{WL}{4}$$

If the beam were uniformly loaded as in Fig. 130(3) we should obtain the following result, the reaction once again being equal to $\frac{W}{2}$ — while the leverage action might be considered as acting through the centre of gravity of the loads equated to single concentrated loads as in Fig. 130(4).

$$\frac{W}{2} \times \frac{L}{2} = \frac{WL}{4}$$

Both the above results accord with the formulæ given in the textbooks.

We can now return to 'the problem of the front member of the canopy, when, with our newly acquired knowledge of bending moments, the working is easy.

Span = 10ft.
Distributed load = 2·00 tons.
Bending moment = $\dfrac{2·00 \times 10}{8}$ = 2·50ft. tons.

Let us now select a suitable channel section from the above information, making use of a working stress of 8 tons to the sq. in. extreme fibre stress.

Maximum bending moment in ft. tons = 2·50.
Maximum bending moment in in. tons = 2·50 × 12 = 30·00.
Modulus of section required = $\dfrac{30·00}{8}$ = 3.75.

Select a 5in. × 2½in. × 10·22lb. channel which has a maximum modulus of section of 4·70.

The side channels do not need to be calculated as they would be manufactured from the same section, although in theory they could be of smaller section.

Should you choose to work to a stress of 10 tons the section could, of course, be lighter and still be in accordance with the requirements of B.S. 449.

Supposing the load is not concentrated at a central point, but is placed as in Fig. 131(1), how would the reaction and bending moments be affected?

Think of two men walking one behind the other with a rafter resting on their shoulders and a bucket slung between them. If the load is placed centrally, each man will bear half the weight, but as the bucket is pushed closer to one man and farther away from the other, the inequality of the load is experienced by both men, until in the end (when the bucket is pushed to the very end of the rafter) the entire load rests on the shoulders of one man only.

The same principle is used in weighing machines. The value of the load at each support is in exact proportion to its distance from that support.

In Fig. 131(1) a load of 10 tons is shown placed at a distance of 4ft. from one pier, the total span being 12ft.

$$\text{Reaction at A} = \frac{8 \times 10}{12} = 6 \cdot 66 \text{ tons.}$$

Reaction at B = $10 \cdot 00 - 6 \cdot 66 = 3 \cdot 34$ tons.

Maximum bending moment calculated from pier A 6·66 tons × 4 = 26·64 tons.

Maximum bending moment calculated from pier B 3·34 tons × 8 = 26·72 tons.

The slight difference in results (they should, of course, be the same) is accounted for by the fact that the decimals used are not quite accurate.

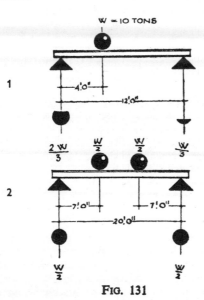

Fig. 131

The above results can be checked in a third way.

$$\text{Maximum bending moment} = \frac{W(a \times b)}{L}$$

The distances a and b represent the respective positions of the load from each pier or support.

$$\frac{10 \cdot 00 \times 4 \times 8}{12} = \frac{320}{12} = 26 \cdot 66 \text{ ft. tons.}$$

It is always better, however, to reason a thing out than to use a formula.

There is one more general example often met with in practice, where two loads of equal weight are symmetrically placed on a beam as in Fig. 131(2). Here the two weights are added together and are then separately designated $\frac{W}{2}$. The reason for this apparently useless manoeuvre becomes clear if we ponder a little. The method of loading and consequent bending is nothing more nor less than two sets of cantilevers, the working being as follows:—

$$5 \cdot 00 \text{ tons} \times 7 = 35 \text{ ft. tons.}$$

Although there is a combined load of 10 tons on the beam, no part of the cross section is subject to a greater bending effort than can be obtained from a leverage of 7ft. If we like to check this from our previous workings we obtain the following result:—

$$\text{Reaction at pier A} \frac{13 \times 5}{20} + \frac{7 \times 5}{20} = \frac{20 \times 5}{20} = 5 \cdot 00 \text{ tons.}$$

If we choose to use the centre of the farther load as the fulcrum we obtain the following working:—

$$(5 \times 13) - (5 \times 6) = 65 \text{ tons} - 30 \text{ ft. tons} = 35 \text{ ft. tons.}$$

All other methods of loading beams are more or less variations of these examples.

Nothing more complicated is likely to be met with in the general run of a builder's work. All the bending moments explained here have been for conditions of ends of beams being freely supported; where, however, the ends of the beams are adequately tied in, either by direct bolted connection with another steel member or by sufficient weight of brickwork as tail load, the stress in the section is considerably reduced due to the added strength given by the means of fixing.

The calculations become complicated and, while the extra difficulty of working for fixed ends or continuous beams is well worth while in a large undertaking, for small works it is usual to assume that the ends of the beams are freely supported.

Where a girder carries an evenly distributed load and a concentrated load in addition, the working is simply the bending moment for each condition added together.

Chapter XIII

TYPICAL APPLICATIONS OF STEELWORK

In practice elementary steelwork construction involves a good deal more than the cut-and-dried application of text-book theory with its set examples and typical instances.

Having mastered the theory, or at least as much of it as is necessary for our purpose, we are now in a position to tackle a comprehensive scheme of steelwork construction such as might be met with in everyday practice.

A customer requires a terrace house altered so that it may be suitable for a bookshop. It is the usual type of terrace house with bay window, narrow entrance passage, and one floor over; part of the ground floor having a coal cellar, as suggested in Fig. 132.

It is not proposed to deal with shopfront construction, but only with the alterations necessary so far as steelwork is concerned.

The suggested plan of the proposed alterations (which should have been submitted to and approved by the customer) is given in Fig. 133.

The bay window, passage and stairs are cleared away (a new staircase being made at the back of the premises), two steel stanchions are placed in position as close to each party wall as possible, and a stout R.S.J. is inserted under the main front wall.

There are two important items which must not be overlooked:

(1) There is a cellar under a portion of the front premises.

(2) On opening up it is found that the passage wall (which has of course to be pulled down) supports the ends of the bedroom floor joists and those of the passage, leaving free ends to be carried.

Having obtain a rough idea of all the factors involved it is now possible to go into a more detailed consideration: to consider each point of steelwork construction as it arises and solve it as a separate problem, finally bringing the whole scheme together as one completed plan.

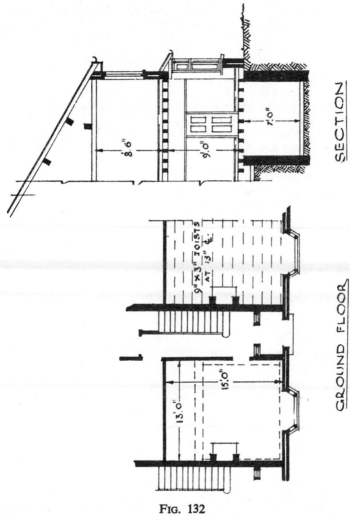

FIG. 132

A constructional engineer, when faced with a large job for a complete steel-framed building, commences his labours at the roof, computing each member floor by floor as he goes down, bringing forward the various loads and wind stresses, until, when he finally reaches the basement, he already has before him a running total of the vast accumulated loads to be carried by the main stanchions and girders.

We, however, are not working in this manner, but selecting a method which will best explain the theory and practice of simple steelwork construction. In many alteration jobs it is not desirable to work from the roof downwards, but to select some key joist, and conduct our investigation of strength from there as a starting point.

In such jobs (which, despite the smallness of the undertaking, may be very complicated) to select an important joist to start with from a shrewdness born of long practice often discloses at once the most unexpected short cuts both in design and costs, or lays bare hidden traps in the construction.

Nothing is more disconcerting for a builder, after he has commenced the job and ordered a full complement of steelwork, to find that he cannot yet proceed by reason of a very important joist having been omitted from his calculations.

It can also be said that nothing saps a customer's confidence more: the job at a standstill, the unexplained waiting, the lame excuses.

Therefore, in any alteration job, search for the key joist first: secondly, wherever a wall is knocked down, there is generally something which has to be put in its place.

Apart from warehouses, books and stationery are among the heaviest goods to be stored and give rise to the greatest concentration of weight on a floor or beam.

The latest edition of the Building Bylaws specifies a load of 200lb. per ft. super of floor area shall be the maximum condition of loading to work to for a book store.

In actual practice it is unlikely that every foot of floor space will be covered with books and stationery; paths must be left open to walk around and in among the stored books for the purpose of handling, but, at the same time, it must be remembered that each and every portion of the floor may in turn be

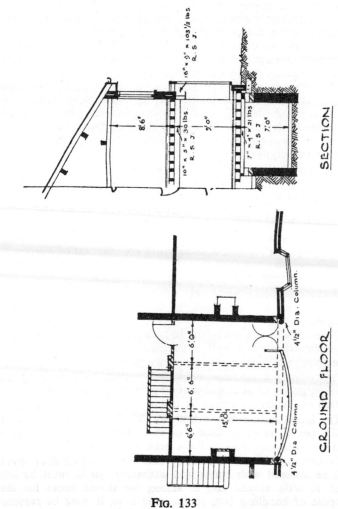

FIG. 133

subject to the full load as the masses of stationery and books are
moved and rearranged from time to time.

Now we know what we are looking for we can tackle the
problem of the first floor storage, not forgetting the added complication of the existing floor joists which have been verified
upon opening up as being 9in. × 3in. spaced at 15in. centres.
It is not a single problem of straightforward design for a specified
load. We must first of all find out if the existing floor joists
will safely take a superimposed distributed load of 200lbs. per
ft. super, and, if not, would it be possible, by shortening the
span of the joists, and judiciously placing intermediate girders,
to make use of the present floor joists without disturbing them:
a great saving in expense if at all feasible.

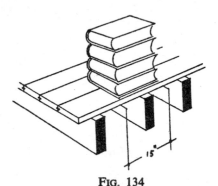

Fig. 134

Fig. 134 indicates one of the floor joists carrying its proportion
of the superimposed load of books and stationery. The diagram
shows that for each 12in. run of joist it carries a superficial area
of 12in. × 15in. or 1¼ft. super, making a distributed load of
1¼lb. × 200lb. = 250lb. per ft. run of span, say 2¼cwt. The
floor joists next to the walls may be taken as bearing half this
weight. The main span is 13ft., making the total load distributed
on one floor joist 13 × 2¼cwt. = 30cwt. in round figures.

The strength of a fir beam is easily arrived at by that old and
trusted formula $W = \dfrac{bd^2}{L}$.

By substitution the following expression is obtained:—

$$W = 30$$
$$b = 3$$
$$d = 9$$
$$d^2 = 81$$
$$L = 13$$

$$30 = \frac{3 \times 81}{13} = 18\cdot54\text{cwt.}$$

$$30\cdot00\text{cwt.} = 18\cdot54\text{cwt.}$$

The result shows that the floor is grossly under strength as was to be expected, seeing that its original purpose was for use as a dwelling house.

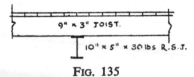

FIG. 135

It will now be necessary to try the formula with the steel joist interposed as in Fig. 135, which halves the span reducing it to 6ft. 6in. and so greatly lessening the bending moment.

$$W = \frac{3 \times 81}{6\cdot50} = 37\cdot50\text{cwt.}$$

This simple calculation has revealed that the existing floor joists are strong enough if supported at mid-span by a girder, which brings in the next question. What shall be the size of the girder?

Fig. 136 shows the load it will have to support, contained by an area of 6ft. 6in. × 15ft. 0in. = 97·50ft. sup. each square foot of which must be capable of supporting 2¼cwt. consisting of the superimposed load of 200lb. plus the weight of the joist and the floor boards. (This load should not be confused with the load of 2¼cwt. per 15in. width superimposed on the wooden joists.)

The total distributed load the girder has to carry is as follows:—97·50 × 2·25cwt. = 219·375cwt., say 11 tons, evenly distributed over a span of 15ft. There is no need to trouble ourselves with the bending moment in this instance.

The steelwork tables show that a 10in. × 5in. × 30lb. R.S.J. will safely support a distributed load of 13 tons, which also allows an adequate margin for the weight of the joist itself (roughly 480lb.), and it is well within the limits of deflection.

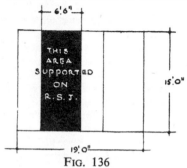

Fig. 136

Although the load on the girder to be placed where the passage wall was removed is slightly less than the previous calculation, it will be practical to use the same girder here, namely 10in. × 5in. × 30lb., thus saving ourselves further calculation, without in any way adding to the cost of the work.

The computation of the intermediate floor girders may now be considered complete and their sizes and weights lettered in on the steelwork scheme: but there remains one more very important consideration.

The placing of the girders has thrown a concentrated load on the back wall of the proposed shop, a load which the original wall of 4½in. brickwork was never intended to support.

The amount of the new load is equal to half the value of the distributed load plus half the weight of the girder itself: 5½ tons plus 2 cwt., say 6 tons in round figures.

Common brickwork in lime mortar may be taken as strong enough (when matured) to support an evenly distributed load of 5 tons per ft. sup. The reaction therefore requires a spread of 6/5 tons = 1·20ft. sup., but the wall is only 4½in. wide, which would result in the following calculation:—

$$\frac{6 \times 12 \times 2}{5 \times 9} = \frac{16}{5} = 3\text{ft. 3in. long.}$$

A padstone 3ft. 3in. long by 4½in. wide would be required to spread the weight suitably, at the same time no extra strength has been allowed to the wall so that it may still support the existing wall over together with the ceiling joists, etc.

The problem is easily resolved by building a brick pier in common brickwork in cement mortar on the side facing the inner room so that it is not seen from the shop.

A pier 3ft. wide and projecting 4½in. will tie into the existing brickwork and provide complete strength, especially if hoop iron ties are used at 3ft. vertical intervals. The same pier construction may be repeated to take the end of the R.S.J. over the passage.

An important point to remember when placing girders on existing brickwork is that although the brickwork may safely take the new load, the wall may yet fail, as would a tall pillar through want of an intermediate support. A safe rule therefore, in the case of all 4½in. walls, is to build a pier whether strict theory requires it or not.

The placing of the girder has brought us to the last consideration before we can be finally satisfied; the safe bearing capacity of the soil.

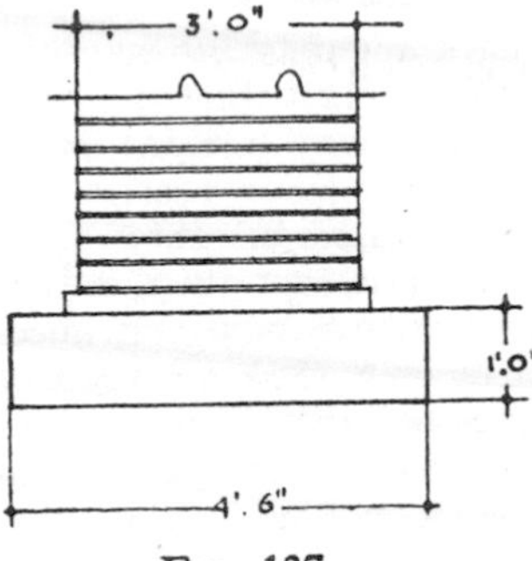

FIG. 137

If the reaction is taken as 6 tons in round figures (which may also be assumed to include the weight of the supporting brickwork) and the safe bearing capacity is 1¼ tons per sq. ft., 4 ft. sup. will clearly be required to spread the load.

The brick pier has already been decided on as being 3ft. wide or the nearest convenient measurement to four bricks, the pier projection is 4½in. It would seem that a concrete footing 4ft. 6in. long by 1ft. 0in. wide with one course of projecting brick footings would meet all requirements, as shown in Fig. 137.

In a heavy construction the original brickwork would undoubtedly be underpinned or a complete new concrete footing inserted, but in this case it would be carrying things to extreme limits besides adding unwarrantably to the costs.

In involved constructions a lead pad formed of 6lb. sheet lead is laid under the ends of the girders so that in final settlement there shall be absolutely even contact between the bottom flanges of the R.S.J. and its bearing.

The 10in. × 5in. R.S.J. chosen reduces the headroom in the shop (which, fortunately, is 9ft. high to ceiling) considerably. The addition of bracketing and plaster will take a full 12in.

Headroom is always an important point to watch. If necessary, use a stronger and heavier section to reduce the depth of the girder, or even two coupled together rather than be cramped for headroom.

Many a good and otherwise competent scheme has been wrecked on the hidden rocks of headroom! It is only when the steelwork has arrived on the site and has been hoisted into position that the terrible reality breaks in upon one.

The logic of commencing with the intermediate girders may seem strange until we realise that these girders are really the key to the calculation of the main girder, in that they bring point loads to bear on the main bressummer. The maximum bending moment cannot be calculated until these factors are known.

But for the intervention of the two intermediate girders the bending moment diagram of the front beam would be represented by a parabola. The two concentrated loads will now turn the bending moment diagram or funicular polygon into a combination of straight line diagram and parabola.

Had the secondary girders combined to form one central load on the main beam, the bending moment for this and the parabola could have been calculated separately and added together. This, however, is not the case; the two intermediate loads each produce a bending moment at points roughly one-third of the span from each support, whereas the parabola shows the maximum bending moment at the centre of the span, the effort gradually diminishing according to the amount of span traversed and in accordance with the formula $\dfrac{wl^2}{8}$. The combined moments are shown in Fig. 138.

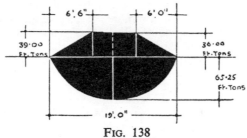

FIG. 138

It will be noticed that the ground floor plan is partially cellared, the floor joists running in the same direction as the first floor and of the same scantling, namely 9in. × 3in. spaced at 15in. centres.

The span of the cellar R.S.J. will only require to be 10ft. The calculation for the girder can be considerably reduced, merely by taking 10/15ths or two-thirds of the previous loading over a span of 10ft. 11 tons × $\frac{2}{3}$ = 7$\frac{1}{3}$ tons over a span of 10ft., say 7$\frac{1}{2}$ tons including weight of girder.

From the tables a 7in. × 4in. × 21lb. R.S.J. is shown to be a suitable section. Here again no bending moment need be calculated; also this time it will not be necessary to trouble ourselves with the load bearing capacity of the brickwork.

The house is of old-fashioned construction and the cellar walls are already built of 14in. brickwork, the inner 4$\frac{1}{2}$in. of which is not at present called upon to support a structural load of any kind.

Due to the spread of the concrete footings it will not be necessary to investigate the bearing value of the soil, but there is one thing which should be done—the size of the padstone should be worked out. Taking the bearing value of brickwork as 5 tons per sq. ft. divided into the reaction of 3·75 tons it would be practical to take this as 1 ft. sup. or a padstone 9in. × 1ft. 6in. long.

A word in passing. The cellar girder will be 10ft. 9in. long, and weigh just over 1½cwt. The ground floor joists will have to be disturbed after all to enable the girder to be handled and hoisted into position; a point to remember when making up the estimate.

The coast is now clear to tackle the problem of the main bressummer. To do this we commence at the roof and work downwards taking each distributed load and point load as we go until we finally arrive at the total load coming on to the girder from all sources, and, equally important, the position of the loads.

The total distributed dead load coming on the bressummer will be half the weight of the slated roof commencing with the ridge, slates, battens, rafters, wind pressure and temporary loads such as snow and rain. Then follows half the weight of the ceiling joists, hangers and plastered ceiling, finishing with the full weight of the common brickwork, making no deductions for windows.

For our purpose the complete weight of the roof may be taken as ¼cwt. per foot super of sloping surface to include wind pressure and temporary loads.

> Length of rafter on slope = 22ft.
> Span 19ft.
> Weight per foot super = ¼cwt.
> Area. 22ft. × 19ft. = 418ft. super.
> Total weight of roof:
> 418 × ¼cwt. = 209cwt., say 11tons.

CEILING MEASURED HORIZONTALLY

Span 19ft.
Half depth = 7ft. 6in.
Weight per foot super = 1cwt.
(This weight is much too heavy but will allow of the roof space being used for tanks or light loads.)
Area of ceiling 19 × 7·50ft. = 142ft. 6in. super.
Total weight of ceiling:
142·50 × 1cwt. = 142½cwt., say 7½tons.

BRICKWORK

Wall area 19ft. × 11ft. high = 209ft. super.
Weight per foot cube = 120lb.

Weight of wall 209 × 9in. × 120lb. =
$$8 \text{tons } 7 \text{cwt., say 9tons approx.}$$

TOTAL DISTRIBUTED LOAD ON GIRDER

Roof 11tons.
 Ceiling 7·5tons.
 Brickwork 9tons = 27·5tons.
  TOTAL COMBINED LOADS COMING ON TO GIRDER
 Distributed load 27·5tons.
  Two separate point loads each of 6tons.

A bending moment diagram used at this juncture will be of tremendous help in clarifying the succeeding calculations.

Examine Fig. 138, where it can be seen at a glance the nature of the problem which now confronts us. To be strictly accurate the point loads are not evenly placed, one being 6ft. 6in. from the end of the span, the other being only 6ft., but in practice, if we take the bending moment for the larger case of leverage, namely, 6ft. 6in., we shall be amply covered as regards the strength of the beam; a more meticulous working would make no difference in cost.

The total bending moment is equal to the maximum length of the ordinate to the parabola, plus the maximum ordinate from the straight line diagram.

Commencing with the straight line diagram we have the following:—

Maximum bending moment =
$$6 \text{ tons} \times 6 \text{ft. 6in.} = 39 \text{ft. tons.}$$
Maximum bending moment for distributed load =
$$\frac{WL}{8} = \frac{27 \cdot 5 \text{ tons} \times 19 \cdot 00}{8} = 65 \cdot 25 \text{ tons.}$$

Combined bending moments =
$$65 \cdot 25 \text{ft. tons}$$
$$39 \cdot 00 \text{ft. tons}$$

Total   104·25ft. tons

Having obtained by calculation the value of the maximum bending moment, we can now equate this to a suitable modulus of section.

Reduce the bending moment from foot tons to inch tons and divide by the safe working stress to arrive at the required modulus of section.

$$\text{Maximum bending moment} = \frac{104\cdot25 \times 12}{8} = 152\cdot38.$$

A suitable joist from the tables is a 16in. × 9in. × 103¼lb. R.S.J., which has a maximum modulus of section of 156·90 and will bear a distributed load of 42·50 tons over a span of 19ft., thus comfortably including for the weight of the girder itself.

This section is particularly suitable due to the breadth of the flange which is 9in. As shown in Fig. 139 the brickwork sits compactly on top of the cover stones. These latter should not be less than 3in. thick, and may be either of precast concrete reinforced with wire mesh, or matured hard York stone.

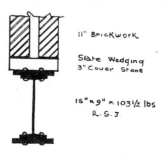

FIG. 139

The girder is a composite one consisting of a 14in. × 5½in. × 40lb. R.S.J. with a 9in. × 1in. steel plate riveted to the top and bottom flanges, making a total weight of 103¼lb. per foot run including rivet heads. The shanks of the rivets, of course, merely replace the weight of the metal drilled out of the plates and flanges.

In such an important structure as a book store, it is preferable to take an extreme fibre stress of 8 tons per sq. in. for all main girders and not to work to a stress of 10 tons per sq. in., which reduces the factor of safety from 4 to roughly 3.

The revised B.S. 449: 1959 Tables more or less admit the truth of this statement in so many words by the reduction they make in their tabular loads once a certain span is passed. They still have to come back to the old working where the estimated deflection must not rise beyond 1-325th of the span.

Had two girders of lighter section been chosen in place of one heavy girder, it would really have necessitated two separate calculations to be absolutely correct; one to define the inner beam, which would receive half the distributed dead load, amounting to 13·75 tons, plus two point loads of 6 tons each, whilst the external girder would be subject to a distributed load of 13·75 tons only.

Where this type of construction is resorted to, it is customary to bind the two girders together by means of cast iron separators and bolts which are fastened through to webs at distances not exceeding five times the depth over flanges and particularly over each support and under each concentrated load as indicated in Fig. 140.

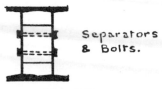

Separators & Bolts.

FIG. 140

The effect is to make the two girders thus bolted together act more or less as one. A tendency to flexure in the inner girder is transferred over the fibres of the outer girder by reason of the strain imposed on the connecting bolts.

Before leaving the beams they must be tested for estimated deflection.

Commence with the floor girders.

Deflection formula $\dfrac{5W1^3}{384\ EI}$

W = 11 tons.
1 = 15ft. = 180in.
E = 12,000 tons.
I = 146·23

$$\frac{5 \times 11 \times 180 \times 180 \times 180}{384 \times 12,000 \times 146 \cdot 23} = \frac{4455 \cdot 00}{9358 \cdot 72}$$

less than $\frac{1}{2}$in.

This may be taken as satisfactory but it is to be noted that the extreme fibre stress has been taken as 8 tons per sq. in. The result is for all practical purposes near enough in view of the fact that the full tabular load for a 10in. × 5in. R.S.J. is 13 tons against 11 tons actual requirements.

Having wandered into the realm of plated girders it is to be noted that the section book warns us that whilst the beam is quite adequate in all respects as regards bending moment and shear value (measured vertically) it requires extra strength in the form of web stiffeners to prevent the web from failing as a pillar with both ends fixed.

The web of ⸱ 14in. × 5½in. R.S.J. is 12·32in. deep and only ·37in. wide, a very slender amount of metal to resist a super-imposed load of 40 tons.

Test first for shear.

Shear value per square inch = 5·50ton.

Reaction at each support = 20·00ton.

Net depth of web = 12·33in.

Net web thickness = ·37in.

Net web area 12·33 × ·37 = 5·56in.³

Shear strength 4·56 × 5·5 = 25ton approx.

Therefore the joist chosen is suitable as regards shear strength.

The calculations for web buckling are very tedious and need not be undertaken in a simple construction. Web stiffeners are standard. It is thus only necessary to inform the manufacturers when placing the order that web stiffeners are required at the same time specifying the exact position where the point loads occur. Maximum shear and with it maximum tendency to web buckling occur at the points of support diminishing in stress as the point of maximum bending moment is approached.

Notice a railway plate girder and it will be seen that vertical angle irons are inserted between the flanges of the joist and concentrated at the ends where the terrific loads are supported, gradually being spaced much wider apart as the centre of the span is reached.

Deflection for the main beam must now claim our attention,

in doing which it forms a secondary check on the correctness of our other workings.

W = 42·50 tons (full tabular value).

E = 12,000 tons.

1 = 19ft. = 228in.

1 = 1255·00.

$$\frac{5 \times 42·50 \times 228 \times 228 \times 228}{384·00 \times 1200 \times 1255·00} =$$

$$\frac{3249 \times 323}{4800 \times 502}$$

Faced with an involved fraction of this nature it will be found a great help to proceed so far by the usual routine of cancelling out, multiplication and division and finally to complete the working by means of logarithms. This method effects a great saving of time and obviates arithmetical errors.

Log.	3249·00	=	3·5117
Log.	323·00	=	2·5092
			6·0209

Log.	4800·00	=	3·6812
Log.	502·00	=	2·7007
			6·3819

Log.	6·0209
Log.	6·3819
	1·6390

Anti-log ·4355. (Note negative index.)

Deflection therefore equals less than $\frac{1}{2}$in.

We now come to the stanchions. It has been decided to use solid steel circular columns as taking up the least room and giving the widest possible window and door space for shop display purposes.

Stanchion caps should be kept as small as possible in order to avoid the effect of undue or accidental leverage. In practice it is more difficult than one might think to place the end of a girder in such a manner on a stanchion cap that the load is transmitted centrally and evenly to the steel shaft. The larger the stanchion cap the wider the area of possible eccentricity.

A stanchion that is placed centrally in a scheme of loading (providing the loads each side of the stanchion are equal in weight and disposition) is much more certain of being free from unintentional eccentricity than a stanchion which is loaded from one side only. The pillars in our example fall into this latter category.

In round figures each of the columns is called upon to support a load of 20 tons. The pillars caps should be made so that they are flush with the external face of the pillar at one side as in Fig. 141 in order that the column may be as close up to the party wall as possible.

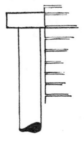

FIG. 141

The shaft itself should be 9ft. long plus sufficient depth to enable the baseplate to come at a convenient dimension below the floor level, say 2ft. extra, making a total length of 1ft. overall.

As a preliminary canter, choose a column 4½in. diameter with an eccentricity coefficient of 1 plus 1·78e (where e equals the arm of eccentricity, in this case taken as 1in.).

However a circular column is calculated, the eccentricity co-efficient must be the same for all axes and radii.

Load to be supported = 20 tons.

Eccentricity $1 + (1·78) 1 = 2·78$.

Equivalent tabular concentric load $20 \times 2·78 = 55·60$ tons.

The tables give 56·70 tons, therefore the section chosen seems entirely suitable. Before, however, being satisfied it should be tested for stress according to its ratio of slenderness.

$$\text{Ratio of slenderness} = \frac{1}{g}$$

$$\frac{11 \times 12}{1 \cdot 125} = \frac{132}{1 \cdot 125}$$

Log.   132 = 2·1206
Log. 1·125 = ·0511
────────
2·0695 = 112·50
────────

The stress allowed for a ratio of slenderness of 113 for the conditions of both ends fixed is 3·65 tons per sq. in.

3·65 × 15·904 (area of column) = log. 3·65 + log. 15·904.

·5623
1·2014
────────
1·7637 = 58·03 tons.
────────

The column chosen has proved to be sufficient as regards ratio of slenderness and permissible stress.

Weight for weight, a circular solid steel column is less economical as regards load carrying capacity than an H section R.S.J. The flanges of a stanchion, being set wide apart by comparison with the single steel shaft of a circular column, afford much greater resistance to bending, thus enabling a higher stress ratio to be used for the same ratio of slenderness.

The cap and base plates are shrunk on to the shaft and are of standard construction.

The load transmitted to the ground would require a superficial area of 13ft. super, taking the safe bearing capacity of the soil as $1\frac{1}{2}$ tons per foot super. The blue brick column should, of course, transmit the load by means of offsets as shown in Fig. 142.

A reasonable thickness for the concrete base would be 12in. and one layer of B.R.C. Fabric No. 10 or similar laid in the bottom of the footing.

The safe pressure on blue engineering bricks may be taken as 10 tons per sq. ft., so that the size of the pier going down into

o

the cellar would be 2ft. super, say 18in. sq. In theory the footing for the pier should be a little larger than that for the right hand column on account of the extra weight imposed by the blue brick pier itself, but since the bearing capacity of the soil has been restricted to $1\frac{1}{4}$ tons per sq. ft., the footing to each pier may well remain equal in size.

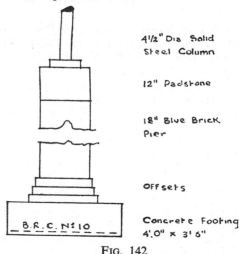

4½" Dia Solid Steel Column

12" Padstone

18" Blue Brick Pier

Offsets

Concrete Footing 4'.0" x 3'6"

B.R.C. Nº 10

FIG. 142

Most alterations (especially where it is a question of turning a building from its accustomed use to an entirely different usage) involve steelwork construction to some extent.

The ability to go on to a job and rapidly seize on the main points of construction is one which every foreman should cultivate.

Chapter XIV

P.C. SUMS EXPLAINED

THE utmost confusion seems to prevail amongst builders and even architects and surveyors as to the correct definition of P.C. Sum, Prime Cost Sum, Provisional Sum, and Provisional Quantities.

A P.C. sum might be defined as a sum of money for specialist work or specialist items which the architect wishes to have at his entire disposal to deal with as he thinks fit, either through the main contractor or not, and irrespective of the latter's contract terms as appertaining to the general contract.

The architect may wish to pay for work done under a P.C. sum in a different manner from that governing the main contract; to dispense with the maintenance period, or to double the maintenance period, to pay in specified instalments, or even to pay in advance. The P.C. sum enables all these things to be done without in any way causing confusion to the main contract.

The P.C. sum is morever an exact estimate obtained from the nominated firm before the completion of the bills of quantities and inserted in the bills exactly as quoted. The name of the selected firm need not be stated in the bills although it nearly always is; neither need the exact figure be put in; the amount may be put in round figures, or a further sum added to the quotation to allow for the other work of an undefined nature which the architect may have in mind.

Suppose the architect has decided to use special made bronze windows. He might obtain an estimate for the windows from Phosphor Bronze Components, Ltd., amounting to £104 16s. 3d. for three windows. This is the amount which would appear in the bills of quantities, set out somewhat as follows: —

1. Allow in estimate the P.C. sum of £104 16s. 3d. for bronze composite windows complete with all fittings, hopper cheeks and steel fixing lugs, supplied and delivered on site by Phosphor

Bronze Components, Ltd., Frustram Lane,
Bownley.   £104 16 3
Add for Profit.

2. Allow for unloading, storing on site until
required for use bronze composite windows,
size 4ft. 6in. × 6ft. 0in. over-all complete as
specified, and return crates carriage paid.

3. Add for hoisting and fixing in position above
bronze windows and building in direct to brick
reveals as the work proceeds, including all cutting and making good brickwork to steel fixing
lugs (No. 10 to each window frame).
Bedding and pointing elsewhere measured.

The P.C. sum carries with it the convention that it shall be
net, save only a discount of 2½ per cent. for cash in the case of a
P.C. sum for labour and materials carried out by a specialist
firm, and 5 per cent. cash for goods supplied only and fixed by
the main contractor.

Thus, in the above example, if the firm supplying the windows
came on to the job and fixed them, the main contractor would
receive 2½ per cent. discount on £104 16s. 3d., that is, £2 12s. 5d.

If the main contractor fixes the windows himself exactly as set
out in the extract from the bill of quantities he would receive a
discount of £5 4s. 9d. in addition to all the other items in the bill.

There are certain rules which should be observed as regards
the obtaining of the correct discount which may be summarised
as follows: —

(a) If the specialist work is carried out in its entirety (both as
regards supply and fixing of materials) by a firm or person
other than the main contractor, then the latter is entitled
to a discount of 2½ per cent.

(b) In the case of specialist goods supplied only (fireplaces, sink
units, baths, w.c. suites, steel windows) and fixed by the
main contractor, a discount of 5 per cent. is due.

(c) All suppliers and fixers in both types of transaction should
plainly state on their quotation that the applicable discounts
have been allowed for, and when eventually the invoices are
rendered, the exact amount of the discount should be shown
on the invoice.

(d) A discount is an amount of money deducted from the principal sum, and not a percentage added.

(e) It follows from (d) that in the case of 2½ per cent. the principal sum is divided into forty equal parts, the supplier agreeing to give one part to the main contractor, retaining thirty-nine parts for himself. In the case of the 5 per cent. discount, the principal sum is divided into twenty equal parts, the supplier agreeing to give one part to the main contractor and to retain nineteen parts himself.

It very often happens in practice that a supplier (called in the contract a nominated supplier) refuses to accord a discount, maintaining that his terms of business have always been net.

In this case the contractor should notify the architect who will give permission to place the order with a firm which will grant the requisite discount. Alternatively the architect will instruct the quantity surveyor to increase the amount of the invoice by a sum equal to one thirty-ninth or one-nineteenth respectively.

Supposing it is a question of special swing doors invoiced at £124 19s. 3d. fixed complete, net.

The quantity surveyor will pass an amount of £128 3s. 4d. made up of £124 19s. 3d., plus £3 4s. 1d. discount. It is easy to see from this that £3 4s. 1d. is one thirty-ninth of £124 19s. 3d. and one-fortieth of £128 3s. 4d.

It is interesting to note that had 2½ per cent. been added to the invoice amount of £124 19s. 3d., the contractor would only have received £3 2s. 6d., a comparatively small error in this instance, but one which would be very important in the case of a large invoice.

A net invoice, therefore, means that under the contract conditions, the main contractor has a voucher for thirty-nine-fortieths of his costs in the case of 2½ per cent. discount, and for nineteen-twentieths of his costs in the case of 5 per cent. discount, the balance remaining being added in each instance by the quantity surveyor when compiling the final account.

Still instancing the example of the special swing doors, supposing that there is a complication when settling the final account due to the fact that the architect only included a P.C. sum of £98 0s. 0d. in the bills of quantities. What should be the "extra", assuming that the builder had inserted a profit of 10 per cent. in his original quantities, and that the increase in price is due solely to the use of a higher quality material and not to any alteration in size or workmanship?

The following would be the correct manner of arriving at the extra charge due to the main contractor.

	£	s.	d.
Amount of invoice received from Pushpush Doors, Ltd. Net	124	19	3
Add for 2½ per cent. discount due to main contractor	3	4	1
	128	3	4
Add 10 per cent. profit as contract	12	16	4
Total Value of Special Swing Doors	140	19	8

Deduct:	£	s.	d.			
P.C. sum for swing doors	£98	0	0			
10 per cent. profit	9	16	0			
	£107	16	0	107	16	0
Extra Cost of Swing Doors				£33	3	8

No mention is made here of the charge by the main contractor for receiving, unloading, storing, returning packing, attendance, etc., because although the cost of the swing doors has been greatly increased, it does not affect in any way the performance of these latter services.

It will be noticed in the above calculation that the builder obtains 10 per cent. profit on his discount as well as on the main sum. This procedure is correct when it is borne in mind that a discount is an amount of money deducted purely for financial consideration of prompt payment, and is in no wise a payment for work done. Should the builder omit to pay his suppliers within the stipulated time he forfeits his right to the discount, and has to pay in full. This contingency, however, does not affect his profit, which remains static.

There is a subtle but important difference between discounts allowed to nominated sub-contractors and nominated suppliers, which is not one of amount only.

In the case of the nominated sub-contractor (that is, where

work and materials are supplied to carry out a complete portion of the job) the discount of $2\frac{1}{2}$ per cent. is not for cash at a month, but for cash within fourteen days of the main contractor receiving the architect's certificate to this effect.

Many nominated sub-contractors completely misunderstand this condition, and wax very indignant when their invoices are not met at the month end. An architect, from many causes, may defer a certificate for six or eight weeks, and at once a dispute arises between the nominated sub-contractor and the main contractor.

It will be found on examination that the nominated sub-contractor has quoted for $2\frac{1}{2}$ per cent. discount cash at a month; that is, he has tendered on different terms from those stated in the contract.

In the case of goods supplied under a P.C. sum the issue is quite straightforward; the contract plainly states that 5 per cent. discount will be allowed for payment within one month of delivering the goods, but on the other hand the main contractor has not the protection of the architect's certificate: to claim the discount he must pay within the prescribed period whether he has received the architect's certificate covering the goods or not.

It often happens that from one cause or another the contractor ignores payment of his specialists and suppliers, with the result that they write in to the architect, who issues them with a certificate for payment direct by the employer. The amount is deleted from the sums due to the main contractor who, of course, loses the advantage of the discount; but should he be debarred from his profit as well?

A moot point.

My personal opinion is (and one which I nearly always act upon) that although the contractor has infringed the contract conditions and loses his right to a discount, he is still personally liable to his client for the sub-contractor's work, even to the extent of making good latent defects within the maintenance period. In the circumstances I consider that his defection in not paying in time is not sufficiently great as to debar him from his profit which, after all, is payment in some measure for being responsible direct to a client for a sub-contractor's work.

P.C. sums are especially important these days. In the case of a large contract innumerable specialists are employed under this heading (heating, ventilating, metal windows, precast floors, specialist pavings, lifts, sprinklers, sanitary fittings, roof lights, hoists, electrical installations, asphalt, pneumatic tubes, internal telephones, speaking systems, strong rooms, and dozens of smaller items).

All of these items might very well be found in one large modern contract, and the question of P.C. sums and discounts becomes one of the highest importance from the point of view of a contractor's estimated profits, and is very often a decisive factor in his original tender determining whether or not he obtains the job.

The P.C. or prime cost sum has this great advantage for the client, that by its use he obtains labour and materials of a specialist nature entirely exclusive of fixer's discount, merchant's discount, and deferred rebates (all with certain qualifications) but nevertheless at a considerably cheaper figure than if he ordered the work direct on his own undertaking, or bought goods by personal choice from a shop or merchant.

A provisional sum is totally different in use and conception from a P.C. sum although the two are so often confused and in some cases are used as interchangeable terms.

A P.C. sum (as already explained) is an exact amount for labour and materials or any goods obtained from a firm tender and inserted in the bills of quantities.

A provisional sum is an estimate (very often rough) for labour and materials and goods, and is generally arrived at by the architect or quantity surveyor from data obtained from similar work.

To use the first example of the metal windows.

Had the architect been pressed for time and unable to obtain a quotation quickly enough, he would have made a rough estimate of the probable cost of the windows, say, £120 0s. 0d. and the following clause would have appeared in the bills of quantities: —

Allow in estimate the provisional sum of
£120 0s. 0d. for metal windows complete with
all fittings to be obtained from a firm to be
selected by the architect £120 0 0

Then would follow the clauses for profit, unloading, fixing, etc., much as before.

On the other hand, at the time of preparing the bills of quantities, the architect might not have decided what he would use, his choice might lie between bronze windows, metal windows with steel pressed panels, mahogany windows, or double windows, should they be set directly into brickwork or in wood frames, should they be in stone facings, or should there be three large windows or four small ones.

In a case like this a provisional sum again meets the requirements but of a different nature to the first quoted instance.

The architect would make an approximate calculation but would include for sufficient money to enable him to carry out his final intentions without exceeding the contract amount, that is, a sum to cover not only the supply of the windows themselves, but also all the structural work connected with them and their immediate surroundings, thus: —

> Allow in estimate the provisional sum of
> £250 0s. 0d. for all work in connection with
> windows to west elevation over main entrance
> doors fixed complete, together with all ancillary
> work to reveals and surrounds to be expended
> as directed by the architect, to be deducted in
> part or in full as required £250 0 0

Here the contractor is not called upon to add anything to the above sum by way of profit. All fixing and profit charges will be set against the sum in the quantities.

In practice, when it comes to carry out this portion of the work, the architect (who by now has settled his details) would obtain exact quotations from the manufacturers for the supply of the windows and a subsidiary quotation for the builder's work complete from the contractor, the total amount being set off against the provisional sum.

A third alternative is to give provisional quantities.

The bill for this part of the work would commence with the heading "provisional", and underneath the last item of all would appear the conclusion "end of provisional items".

Provisional quantities fall exclusively to the quantity surveyor to prepare. In the case of the examples in hand, he would take off quantities under the following headings and insert them in the bill as though they were taken direct from the finished detail drawings.

Steel windows with size and description, unloading, storing

and returning crates, fixing in position, cutting and pinning fixing lugs, bedding and pointing, inner sills, outer sills, lintels, heads, centres, reveals internal and externals, glass according to size, weight and description, painter.

All of the above would appear under the one heading, but sometimes are distributed in trade order.

The object of provisional quantities is not only to provide for undetermined work but also to obtain competitive rates. When the work is eventually carried out, the actual job is entirely remeasured and priced at the rates given in the bills or as near as possible. The whole cost is then added to the final account and the total value of the provisional quantities deducted.

The objection to a provisional sum in round figures is that there may not be rates in the bills to cover the work as executed, and the contractor hankers after daywork rates.

It is unfair to the client to allow daywork rates for work which should be carried out at competitive rates during the course of the contract. Daywork rates (except in special circumstances) are for carrying out operations of an isolated or jobbing nature.

In civil engineering contracts essentially the same rules govern the use of P.C. and provisional sums, save that the discount is generally (but not always) confined to $2\frac{1}{2}$ per cent.

Chapter XV

NOTES ON REINFORCED AND
PRESTRESSED CONCRETE

WHEN looking at a massive reinforced concrete structure, such as a bridge, a dam, or a generating station, it is difficult to remember that only a short time previously the members were in a liquid state, and, in fact, that the whole building was poured from a bucket.

A steel viaduct, one of those gigantic structures used to support main railway lines, or a station roof, with its multiplicity of trellis and arched beams, also has the same attendant peculiarities of construction, in that all its members were prepared from steel which was once in a liquid form: in the case of concrete the liquid was cold, whilst with steel it was hot – an unexpected similarity not often thought about.

The steel skeletons of our great modern buildings are, in so many words, "precast", in that they are fashioned from liquid metal which is cast into ingots from which the various standard sections are squeezed between giant rollers, eventually to be hoisted and fixed on the site, in almost the same way that recent practice deals with large precast reinforced concrete structures, and the huge prestressed beams to which the building and civil engineering industries have become accustomed. The foregoing is an over-simplification, but the essential likeness of manufacture, design, and techniques of erection are the same. It is a very important thing to grasp if we are to understand the basis of design underlying reinforced and prestressed concrete; two materials (or, rather, two totally different uses of the same materials) which appear to differ so radically from steelwork construction with its well-defined tables and choice of standard sections.

Concrete may be constructed to any section with equal facility, either on site or at the factory. This gives the designer much greater scope in obtaining the exact theoretical section and profile, which he needs according to his computation of strength. It does not follow that the exact theoretical member is the cheapest, or even the most practical, but, in large jobs, this consideration does not always prevail.

The quality of concrete (and with it its final strength) starts with the materials, which must be clean and pure. The *cement* will be looked after by the manufacturer and need cause no worry, provided that it is kept absolutely dry, either in bags or in a bulk holder, and stored in such a manner that supplies are used up in the exact order of their delivery. The different kinds of cement in use on one job should be kept separate and designated by a large *sign-board* stating the nature of the cement, and placed prominently before each store in such a manner that even the most happy-go-lucky labourer cannot miss it. The following are the most usual cements to be found on any one job at a time.

ORDINARY PORTLAND CEMENT
RAPID-HARDENING PORTLAND CEMENT
BLAST-FURNACE CEMENT
LOW-HEAT PORTLAND CEMENT
COLOURED CEMENTS

It is ideal to have separate mixers for each type of cement, but since this is seldom possible in practice, a strict ritual of washing-out mixers should be impressed on all the gangers so that, at the change-over, "the little bit left in the can" is not used in the new mix. This simple precaution will undoubtedly save many hours' work cutting out defective concrete with a pneumatic pick, and also gains the confidence of the resident engineer.

Aggregates and sand for important works should all be washed and placed in bins with prominent sign-boards as for the cement.

Water should be absolutely pure and fit for drinking. A supply which comes direct from a well, stream or pool should be analysed by a public analyst well in advance of the work commencing.

With fresh cement, clean, washed aggregates, and pure water, first-class concrete is assured, always providing that the engineer's specification for each part of the work is strictly obeyed.

A warning word must be interposed about site tests for materials and concretes. The tendency these days is for tests to become a fetish, so much so that more importance is often attached to the tests than to the job.

The tests devised and advocated are excellent *for the laboratory* to enable engineers to understand the physical and chemical properties of the materials they are using, and from the data so obtained to invent formulae for the practical work of construction under ideal conditions; but sites are not ideal, quarries are not ideal, gangers are not ideal, labourers are careless, steel fixers misplace reinforcement, the very best cement is not always in prime condition, water (which was crystal-pure at the commencement of the job) becomes polluted three days later, before it is detected; each lorry-load of sand contains a different water content, the batch-mixer is not reading correctly, and the wrong gauge-box has been in use all the morning before the foreman gets round to it, sees it and explodes. All these possibilities (and I am not saying that they would all come together – God forbid!) militate against laboratory conditions and thus nullify tests which are ideal in the laboratory, but become a waste of time on the site.

Foremen are expected to make every conceivable kind of test – grading aggregates, bulking sand, moisture content, purity of water, quality of cement, test cubes, test beams, and, finally, the slump test. A whole laboratory of apparatus goes with the tests; chemist's scales, kitchen scales, kilogramme weights, avoirdupois weights, syphon can, glass measuring cylinder, graded in milligrammes, test tubes, filters, metric rods, steel moulds, Le Chatelier outfit, slump cone, and, last of all, a pycnometer.

Of all this array of apparatus and tests, there are only two of real value on the job: purity of water, which will be carried out by a qualified chemist (the test should be unnecessary where the water comes from public mains) and the *slump test*, the most comprehensive and practical of all tests, and the oldest.

It indicates the water content of the concrete *as mixed*, taking the bulking of sand, moisture content of aggregates, and proportion of sand to gravel in its stride. If the slump is correct there is nothing else to worry about, other things being equal. The test is simple and self-evident, and may be applied quickly to each batch of concrete if so desired.

To carry out the test, concrete is taken at random from a mixer and put into a small steel container, shaped like a milk churn, as indicated in Fig. 143. The mould is made to standard dimensions, being 8in. diameter at the base, tapering to 4in. diameter at the top, and 12in. deep. There are two stout supporting toes and two handles are fixed to the sides. With the open-ended cone goes a standard steel rod for punning, made from a bar $\frac{5}{8}$in. diameter and

24in. long. The mould is filled in 3in. layers, each layer being tamped steadily twenty-five times until the concrete oozes over the top of the cone, when it is scraped off level, after which the mould is lifted vertically and as steadily as possible. The concrete which is

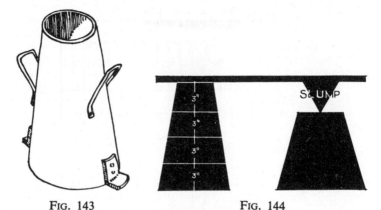

FIG. 143   FIG. 144

thus turned out, slumps, as shown in Fig. 144. A rod is then placed and levelled across the top of the mould, the distance between the underside of the level rod and the top of the slumped pile of concrete is measured in inches, which dimension should be in accordance with the engineer's specified slump. The complete operation should be carried out on a perfectly level surface, and as gently as possible, so that gravity or jolting does not interfere with the efficiency of the test.

It will be observed that the engineer's specified slump is in accordance with the size of the aggregate, the comparative fineness of the mix, and the position in which it is intended to place the concrete. In heavy mass concrete for foundations, an engineer might be content with a 3in. slump; he knows that the concrete can be easily placed and worked; there will be practically no reinforcement to work around. On the other hand, in beams, cantilevers and floors, where there may be two parallel layers of steel rods with intervening shear members, not only will the aggregate itself be of a smaller type, but the mix will have to be sloppier to enable it to be worked and punned around the mesh of steelwork.

It is as well to remember throughout the tests that *cement* is the governing factor in all concretes. However perfectly chosen the gravel and sand, however thoroughly weighed, watered and mixed,

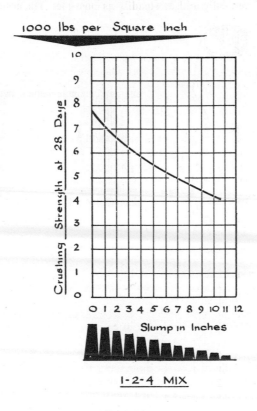

FIG. 145

unless the cement is in perfect condition, you will have wasted your time.

An exaggerated importance these days is given to the *water-cement ratio*, that is, the exact ratio between 1 cwt Portland cement and the actual weight of water used. As an example, if the engineer has specified a water–cement ratio of ·71 the working is as follows:

$$·71 \times 112\text{lb.} = 79·52\text{lb.}$$
1 gallon of water weighs 10lb.
$$79·52\text{lb.} = 7·952 \text{ gallons}$$
8·00 gallons

The above working is a sheer waste of time, because the ratio so painstakingly arrived at is the *net volume* of water; it takes no account of residual water in sand and gravel. This differs from load to load, and even hour to hour, according to whether the aggregates have been lying on the pile and have had time to dry off or not.

And yet the water content is important, as shown in the remarkable graph depicted in Fig. 145, where a 1–2–4 mix is plotted for all slumps from 0 to 12in. The resultant crushing strengths at 28 days are given progressively. Thus, concrete with a 6in. slump has a crushing strength of 5,250lb./in.², whereas with a 1in. slump it is just over 7,000lb./in.². These are ideal results, obtained in the laboratory. Too much importance should not be given to such results, as, at the end of a year, all the crushing strengths for the

CRUSHING STRENGTH						
	I DAY	3 DAYS	7 DAYS	28 DAYS	I YEAR	2 YEARS
TESTS MADE ON 6" CUBES 1-2-4 MIX	POUNDS PER SQUARE INCH					
	1025	3300	4790	5850	7465	7710
	1150	3360	5040	6405	7560	7340
	1180	3265	5010	5910	6875	7620
MEAN VALUES	1120	3310	4945	6055	7300	7555

FIG. 146

same mix, irrespective of the slump, are about the same as shown in the informative table (Fig. 146). It will be noted that up to 28 days the strength increases rapidly, and thereafter very slowly. It must be emphasised that, in the graph shown, the water content is by slump and not ratio.

Fig. 147 gives a diagrammatic view of the materials unmixed and, finally, shaken down into the finished concrete. An allowance of 20 per cent. in the volume of sand for bulking increases the volume of

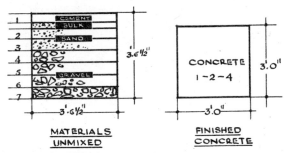

FIG. 147

the unmixed materials, so that a cube, roughly 3ft.-6½in. side, makes a volume of finished concrete into a cube of 3ft.-0in. side. The cement should be so thoroughly mixed with the sand that it forms a mortar, binding the aggregate together, whilst the grading of the aggregate and sand should be such that, by adequate compaction or vibration, the articles slide down against each other until all the voids are full and solid, forming a homogeneous mass like a natural stone.

A further practical help in making good concrete is a *mix board* (Fig. 148). The notice-board should be made of 1¼in. T. & G. square-edge boards solidly framed up so that it does not warp, and painted matt white with black lettering, say 3in. high. The mix, sand, cement, and aggregate notices should be on separate battens which slide into end clips, so that the backboard will serve for any specification. The board should be set up adjacent to each mixer at eye level. Where several different concretes are in use at the same time, these boards are especially valuable. The little extra trouble entailed in their provision ensures that the gang know what it is doing, and it engenders confidence in the resident engineer and clerk of works. The board does not lose its usefulness if the contract is being carried out using ready-mixed concrete, but rather the reverse.

P

We now come to the question of *test cubes*, generally called for in the specification, and the cost of which the contractor should have allowed for in the tender. (It is always worthwhile checking this point.) Specimen cubes, taken from the actual mix, are called for, each being 6in. square on face, made up in accurate steel moulds provided for the purpose, and given over to a physical laboratory to test. The proven strength of the cube at 28 days should not be less than that demanded in the specification. It is of no practical

FIG. 148

value to test concrete before it has attained a maturity of 28 days.

Some civil engineering specifications make an onerous demand of the contractor, in that they require him to cut out and remove all concrete which does not comply with the specified standards, as shown by the results obtained from the test cubes. It is therefore of the utmost importance to insist that all test cubes and tests of whatever description shall be carried out in the presence of the resident engineer or Clerk of Works and a daily signature obtained for all slump tests.

Nothing of use can be learnt from a test cube until 28 days have elapsed, by which time the building, or that portion of it, is probably completed. The concrete in question has possibly been placed deep in the foundations or in the centre of a main beam long before the stipulated 28 days have expired. Should the test cubes prove defective, it is difficult to see what can be done about it, especially if the foreman has signatures for the site routine tests. The use of test cubes, therefore, can only be a partial proof. The discipline involved is worth more than the actual test.

Only a passing word can be said on *shuttering and formwork*. There are many excellent systems of patent steel forms, supports and braces, but, in the end, whatever the patent system in use, they all have to be supplemented by timber at one stage or another. I am of the opinion that timber is far and away the best, and also the most economical, form of shuttering.

The design and erection of timber formwork is an art in itself. There are certain rule-of-thumb principles which apply to any job, and, if followed on all occasions, they will ensure an accurate structure, level, and true.

Formwork should be designed from the point of view of strength, ease of erection and dismantling, facility for carting from job to job, and "number of lives".

Beam soffits should never be less than 2in. stuff, beam sides $1\frac{1}{2}$in., column sides $1\frac{1}{2}$in., flooring soffits $1\frac{1}{4}$in., and no joist supports or struts less than 6in. × 2in. Column yokes 4in. × 3in. and bearing boards not less than 3in. thick. Keep all shuttering thoroughly cleaned and well oiled. Bolts and nuts should have plenty of washers available. The various lining boards for small or special surfaces are seldom worth re-using except in the case of aluminium-faced plywood, or boards lined with aluminium sheet.

Shuttering should be designed to sustain not only the weight of the wet concrete, but also a moving load and impact. It should be able to support a man and barrow-load of concrete, or the sudden shock of concrete tipped from a chute or skip. Insert plenty of loose panels in the column sides to allow for ease in the placing and adjustment of the steel reinforcement and also room for adequately working the concrete. Too much time cannot be spent in ensuring that columns are set dead plumb and that beams are absolutely level with the soffits slightly cambered, so that when the weight of the concrete bears on it, the soffit will not only keep level, but carry a slight permanent curvature. All fixtures such as brackets, pipe collars, syphons, flanges, penstock bolts, holes for mains and conduits, must, of course, be very accurately marked on the formwork itself, and fixtures which have to be cast in with the concrete, adequately supported, to ensure that they are not displaced during the progress of the work.

The requirements of the specification for stripping formwork should be strictly followed. Never take a risk because the formwork is wanted for use elsewhere. If there are no directions in the specification, it is a good rule to leave all shuttering, of whatever nature, for a minimum period of 5 days, large-span soffits and props 21

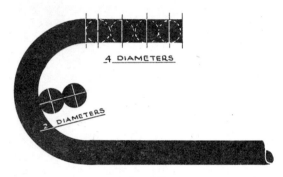

FIG. 149

days, wide-span floors 21 days, and cantilever beams and overhanging balconies 28 days.

In the case of small light weights, and works with a span not exceeding 10ft. 0in. the use of rapid-hardening cement may allow the earlier stripping of formwork, but for heavy works, the longer the concrete is supported, the better.

Reinforcement generally comes on to the job ready bent, hooked, and bundled, but it is as well to have a few spare bars of all diameters, both for high tensile and ordinary reinforcement. It is maddening to find that a bundle which should have contained fifty-four $\frac{7}{8}$in. diameter bars, only contains thirty-four. To avoid loss of time the spare bars may be brought into use, and the steelwork supplier notified accordingly. Spare bars are also useful where it is found that the steelwork drawings and bending schedules will not, in fact, work in with the job, so that the bars have to be adjusted. In all such cases, the resident engineer must, of course, be notified before proceeding. The work in question may possibly be an "Extra", when a signature should be obtained from the Clerk of Works against full written particulars and a little sketch if necessary.

Hooks should be set out as indicated in Fig. 149. The radius of the bend should be equal to 2 diameters of the bar, whilst the straight part of the hook should be equal to 4 diameters. Thus, a $\frac{3}{4}$in. diameter bar would have a bend of $1\frac{1}{2}$in. radius, and a straight projection beyond the semicircular a bend of 3in. Suppliers of reinforcing steel often give away a useful table of dimensions showing the extra length of bar required to be added to the straight in order to form single or double hooks according to each diameter.

Reinforcement should be unloaded in bundles and placed as near the work as possible, each bundle being deposited in order of use. When disposing of the bundles, make certain that the high tensile reinforcement is stored in a separate place, especially as it often happens that the mild steel bars, and the high tensile, are cut to similar lengths, bends, and hooks on the same job. High tensile bars which are twisted, grooved, or indented are frequently cut straight without hooks.

Sheet reinforcement mostly comes flat but is sometimes rolled. Here again it is a wise precaution to have a few spares if the job is of any size. In small jobs there is seldom any error in the number of sheets delivered.

Conveniently with the unloading and stacking of the reinforcement can go the preparation of small concrete distance pieces and spacers, shown in Fig. 150. They should be cast in trays say, 1in., $1\frac{1}{2}$in., 2in., and $2\frac{1}{2}$in. deep, according to the cover required in the specification. About fifty in a tray can very easily be cast. The tray should be laid on a flat, smooth board, lined with well-oiled concrete paper and divided into the requisite number of blocks by means of small slips, say 2in. $\times$ $\frac{1}{2}$in. for a 2in. cover. Each spacer or cover block should be 2in. $\times$ 2in. by thickness of cover and have two lengths of stout tying wire (set at right angles) cast in. For floor and sheet reinforcement it is advisable to increase the size of the blocks to 4in. $\times$ 4in. All floor reinforcement should be well lifted up from the soffit; to ensure this a fair-sized pad of concrete is required.

Having briefly covered the methods involved and the materials to be used in the manufacture of concrete, it is possible to consider its application in the use of reinforced and prestressed concrete.

It is not proposed to go over the ground again where the principles and conditions of structural mechanics apply equally to reinforced concrete and steelwork construction. It will be assumed

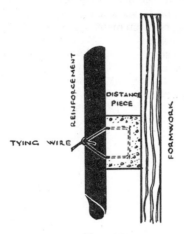

FIG. 150

that Chapters IX to XIII, in which the meaning of bending moment, stress, shear, neutral axis, modulus of section, moment of inertia, etc., are explained in some detail, have been read and understood.

It will readily be comprehended that the physical actions brought into play on a beam or stanchion, by the imposition of a load, are the same whatever the type of material or system of construction may be used. It is only the method of resisting the strain which differs. Thus, a central load of 10 tons placed on a beam induces exactly the same bending moment, tension, compression and shear, whether the beam is timber, wrought iron, steel, reinforced or prestressed concrete. It is the manner of resisting these forces which requires different calculations and disposition of material.

REINFORCED CONCRETE

THERE is one peculiarity in all concrete calculations which must first of all be explained. We have been accustomed so far to dealing with steelwork stressed to 8 tons/in.²; concrete calculations are always stated in lb./in.², adding to the cumbersomeness of the mathematical work. There is a very good reason for this, however; stresses developed in concrete for structural purposes are considerably smaller than those allowed in steel design (as one would expect, since steel is so much stronger a material). In order to arrive at a suitable unit of stress for both materials, lb./in.² have been resorted to. It is quite easy once familiarity has been obtained in use. It should be noted that some engineers prefer to describe the bending moment and moment of resistance as lb./in., whereas others reverse the order and write in. lb.; it makes no difference to the calculation, of course, but it is as well to select one notation and keep to it.

The first notation of lb., in., will be used throughout for concrete calculations.

Example   Stress in steel   8 tons/in.²

$$8 \times 2{,}240\text{lb.}$$
$$17{,}920\text{lb./in.}^2$$

From the above a further complication follows in that all values for bending moments must be reduced to the same terms.

Example   Bending moment   30 tons ft.

$$30 \times 2{,}240\text{lb.} = 67{,}200\text{lb. ft.}$$
$$67{,}200 \times 12 = 806{,}400\text{lb. in.}$$

Reinforced concrete requires us to deal with two distinct materials, one of which is very strong in tension. The other is so weak that, for all practical purposes, the tensile strength can be taken as nil. When it comes to compressive strength, concrete shows that it takes nearly 6,000lb./in.² to crush it at 28 days maturity. Steel, on the other hand, will support a load of 28 to 32 tons/in.² Refer to Fig. 146, which gives the tabulated increases for a 1–2–4 mix from 1 to 28 days, and, finally, at the end of 1 and 2 years.

A simple concrete beam therefore consists of two elements with a great disparity of strength between them. It is obvious that a beam which is composed of two such unsuitable materials (as would appear at first sight) is going to prove difficult to calculate.

Refer to Fig. 86 (p. 137) which shows the neutral axis and the distribution of the tension and compression in a simple steel beam. Now compare the same diagram with Fig. 151, which shows the disposi-

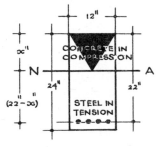

Fig. 151

tion of the stresses in a simple reinforced concrete beam. There is not much difference, except that the bottom half appears to be missing, whilst the neutral axis is not in the centre of the section or centroid.

For demonstration purposes it will be convenient to adopt the following values of concrete and steel. In all cases the mix is assumed to be 1–2–4. These values produce an excellent and economic beam in practice for all ordinary purposes.

Structural engineers make use of much higher compressive strengths for concretes, up to 1,700lb./in.² and beyond, whilst they frequently use a tensile steel stress of 18,000 to 25,000lb./in.², or even 30,000lb., raising the modula ratio from 15 to 10. In this connection it is worth noting that many of the patent systems of precast reinforced concrete flooring have adopted a stress for concrete in compression of 1,000lb./in.², and steel in tension of 18,000 to 25,000lb./in.². After this chapter has been assimilated it will be easy to check the published tables of most of the patent flooring systems. They are essentially lintols of small depth fixed singly, side by side, or two small lintols connected (hollow floors) and laid in pairs.

Working Stresses

Concrete in compression	..	..	750lb./in.²
Concrete in shear	..	..	..	40lb./in.²
Steel in tension	..	..	..	16,800lb./in.²
Modula ratio ..	..	..	..	15

It has just been said that the tensile strength of concrete is nil; a statement made for convenience only in explaining the working of a simple beam. Engineers do, in fact, attribute a certain elasticity to concrete, and, in order to arrive at a working solution for the two materials, have assumed that concrete is 1/15th as elastic as steel. This assumption is called by engineers the modula ratio.

The incidence of shear must also be taken into account. The effects of shear are illustrated in Figs. 90 and 91 on p. 143. With concrete the effects of horizontal and vertical shear are more visible than with steelwork, and are inclined to show on the face of the beam as a diagonal shear, the resultant of the two equal stresses. Fig. 152 provides the theoretical lines of the resultant diagonal

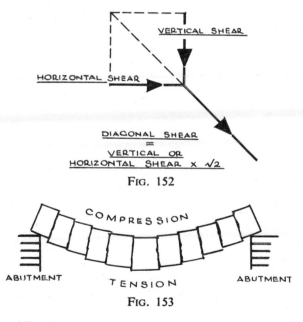

VERTICAL SHEAR

HORIZONTAL SHEAR

DIAGONAL SHEAR
=
VERTICAL OR
HORIZONTAL SHEAR × √2

FIG. 152

COMPRESSION

ABUTMENT   TENSION   ABUTMENT

FIG. 153

shear, whilst Fig. 153 shows the more likely actual result on a concrete beam subjected to extreme bending. The voussoir-like fractures are greatly exaggerated in the illustration, but, despite the fact that, *theoretically*, the beam should show shear marks on the face at an angle of 45 deg. to the soffit, the action of vertical shear would seem to predominate. It is a mathematical and physical fact that vertical and horizontal shear are *bound to be equal*, the resultant always being the value of the vertical or horizontal shear times $\sqrt{2}$, as clearly exemplified in Fig. 152.

Let us now take a simply supported reinforced concrete beam as in the diagrams in Figs. 154 and 155. The span is 20ft. 0in. and the equivalent central load is 5 tons. Bending moment in lb. ft. is

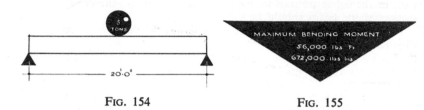

FIG. 154	FIG. 155

arrived at as follows. (Note how the bending moment is dealt with at this stage, namely lb./ft.)

$$\frac{WL}{4} = \frac{5 \times 20 \times 2,240}{4} = 56,000\text{lb. ft.}$$

We thus know that a force of 56,000lb. ft. has to be resisted by a beam of the dimensions shown in Fig. 151, which gives a section 12in. wide by 24in. deep *as probably being strong enough.*

One of the main difficulties of structural engineering is, that profiles and sizes of members have to be assumed first, and checked for strength afterwards. There are no means of deriving sections and profiles by direct computation, not even with simple compressive stresses on stanchions. Engineers, by constant practice, are generally very shrewd in their choice of a preliminary section. In large works, however, arriving at a suitable section is often very arduous, the member having to be rejected again and again.

It is good practice to deal with the concrete first. Everything that was said about variation of stress and the position of the neutral axis in Fig. 86 can be repeated about Fig. 151. The only difficulty here is that the position of the neutral axis is unknown. It will be necessary to resort to simple algebra, but before doing so note care-

fully that the last two inches of the concrete are of no use structurally; they are simply a cover for the steel rods. The beam is therefore
reduced to 22in. in depth.

The stress in the top half of the beam must clearly be equal to
that in the lower half, below the neutral axis, otherwise the beam
would split.

It is an important consideration that the modula ratio shall be
taken as 15, which means that the compressive strength in the upper
portion of the beam must be in the ratio of 1/15th to that of the
steel in the lower portion of the centroid, as, strictly, the cross-
section of the beam should be called.

To reduce the working to algebraical terms, the neutral axis is
situated at x in. from the top of the beam, and (22in. − x in.) from
the bottom of the beam, or, rather, to the centre of the reinforcement, as shown in Fig. 151.

Referring to the table of working stresses and the modula ratio,
the distance of the neutral axis from the top of the beam compared
with the distance from the bottom of the beam is given by the simple
equation:

$$\frac{x}{(22 - x)} = \frac{750}{\dfrac{16,800}{15}}$$

This calculation is not nearly as formidable as it seems at first
sight. If a slide rule is available, now is the time to use it; alternatively, logarithms are most excellent for this type of work. The
following example is worked out step by step with the aid of logarithms.

$$\frac{x}{(22 - x)} = \frac{750 \times 15}{16,800}$$

$$\frac{x}{(22 - x)} = \frac{11,250}{16,800}$$

$$x = (22 - x)\frac{(11,250)}{16,800}$$

Log 11250 = 4·0511
Log 1680 = 4·2253
                  ———————
(*Note negative index*) −1·8258   (Subtract for division)

Anti Log $- 1 \cdot 8258 = \cdot 6695$

$\qquad = \cdot 67$ (for all practical purposes)

$\qquad x = (22 - x)(\cdot 67)$

$\qquad x = 14 \cdot 74 - \cdot 67x$

$\qquad 1 \cdot 67x = 14 \cdot 74$

$$x = \frac{14 \cdot 74}{1 \cdot 67}$$

Log $14 \cdot 74 = 1 \cdot 1685$

Log $1 \cdot 67 = \cdot 2227$

$\qquad\qquad \overline{ \cdot 9458}$

Anti Log $\cdot 9458 = 8 \cdot 826$

$\qquad\qquad = 8 \cdot 8$in.   (for all practical purposes)

It is now possible to complete the stressed section shown in Fig. 156 in which it will also be noted that, in order to obtain the

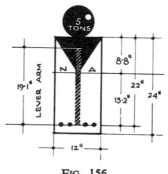

FIG. 156

lever arm of the centroid, it is necessary to calculate the distance from the centre of gravity of the compression area to the centre of gravity of the tensile area, that is, the centre of the steel rods. Referring to Fig. 87 (p. 138), it is here demonstrated that the centre of gravity of a triangle is two-thirds the distance along a line set up at right angles from the base and passing through the apex of the triangle; the distance being measured from the apex, not forgetting that in Fig. 156 the apex is inverted.

The length of the lever arm can now be obtained.

$$22\text{in.} - \frac{8\cdot8\text{in.}}{3}$$

$$22\text{in.} - 2\cdot9\text{in.} = 19\cdot1\text{in.}$$

With the length of the lever arm known it is possible to compute a moment of resistance strong enough to resist the bending moment of 56,000lb./ft., as shown in Fig. 155, remembering that before the bending moment can be used it must be reduced to lb. in. from which the following equation results.

56,000 × 12lb. in. = Total steel tension × lever arm
56,000 × 12lb. in. = 16,800 × 19·1 × area of steel

$$\text{Area of steel} = \frac{56,000 \times 12}{16,800 \times 19\cdot1}$$

Log 56,000 = 4·7482
Log 12   = 1·0792
            ───────
             5·8274

Log 16,800 = 4·2253
Log 19·1   = 1·2810
            ───────
             5·5063

Log 5·8274
Log 5·5063
──────────
Log ·3211

Anti Log ·3211 = 2·094in.²

Four $\frac{7}{8}$in. diameter bars give a total cross-sectional area of 2·405in.². In theory, four $\frac{13}{16}$in. diameter bars would be sufficient, giving a total cross-sectional area of 2·074in.². The $\frac{13}{16}$in. bars are not a usual section, whilst the $\frac{3}{4}$in. bars would have insufficient cross-sectional area. Practical considerations always come first in reinforced concrete work.

Having determined the maximum moment of resistance it will be necessary to investigate the shear values as in the following computation.

Section for shear   12 × 22 × 40lb. = 10,560lb.

The shear is at the maximum at the point of support and is there-fore equal to 2½ tons or 7,600lb. It can be seen without further cal-culation that the concrete alone is more than strong enough, with a very conservative shear stress of 40lb./in.². In practice two of the bars would be turned up at an angle of 45 deg. at the ends to act as

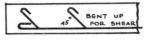

FIG. 157

shear bars as indicated in Fig. 157. Incidentally, it is unnecessary to carry the bars right through to the end of the beam, due to the rapidly decreasing bending moment.

It will be useful to compare the length of the lever arm with the effective depth.

$$\frac{19 \cdot 1}{22} = \frac{\text{Log } 19 \cdot 1}{\text{Log } 22} \quad \frac{1 \cdot 2810}{1 \cdot 3424}$$

$$\text{Anti Log } -1 \cdot 9386 = \cdot 8682 = \cdot 87$$

This value (·87) for the lever arm can safely be used in practice for all simple beams with tension reinforcement only.

Concrete columns are easy to calculate in that, for all stresses within the ratio of slenderness (virtual length divided by effective diameter or diagonal), the deciding factors of strength are con-cerned with compression only in the concrete, plus compression only on the steel. It is usual to take the area of concrete within the steel core as being available to resist compression.

Fig. 158 shows the cross-section of a concrete column 10ft. 0in. high with a concentric load of 40 tons including its own weight. Assume a column 14in. × 14in. in which the steelwork has a cover of 2in. all round.

Cross-sectional area of concrete available within the core

$$10\text{in.} \times 10\text{in.} = 100\text{in.}^2$$

Concrete in compression $= 100 \times 750\text{lb.} = 75,000\text{lb.}$

33·50 tons (say)

Steel is plainly necessary if the column is not to be increased in size so that it becomes too unwieldy for our purpose.

The modula ratio in this instance means that the area of steel should be 1/15th that of the concrete, which produces the following useful equation.

$$\text{Total area} = A$$
$$\text{Steel area} = a_s$$
$$750(A - a_s) + 15(a_s \times 750) = 750(A + 14a_s)$$
$$40 \text{ tons} = 750 (100 + 14a_s)$$
$$40 \text{ tons} = 75,000 + 10,500a_s$$
$$89,600\text{lb.} = 75,000 + 10,500a_s$$
$$14,600 = 10,500a_s$$
$$\frac{14,600}{10,500} = a_s = 1\cdot391\text{in.}^2$$

In actual practice a minimum of 1 per cent. of the effective concrete sectional area for the steel bars would be chosen, even if the column were strong enough without reinforcement.

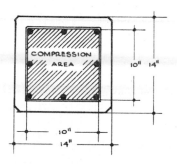

Fig. 158

For Fig. 158, No. 8 $\frac{1}{2}$in. diameter bars would be sufficient giving a total cross-sectional area of $1\cdot570$in.^{2}. The bars would be bound with $\frac{3}{8}$in. diameter hoops spaced at 6in. centres in order to resist any tendency of the reinforcement to spring outwards.

PRESTRESSED CONCRETE

PRESTRESSED concrete is divided into two main classes: post-tensioned and pre-tensioned, meaning that, in the first case, all wires and cables are tensioned after the concrete has set, and, in the second case, that the wires are tensioned first and the concrete cast around them, the wires being cut after the concrete has hardened. The result is exactly the same, whatever method of prestressing is resorted to. Pretensioning is eminently suitable for factory work in the manufacture of floor slabs, railway sleepers, lintols, pylons, piles, trusses. This method is seldom used on the site.

Post-tension is the chief method for site works and is the process which will be described here. It is practically the only method used for prestressed beams of large span whether manufactured at the factory and carted to the job, or the concrete is cast *in situ*.

For an easier understanding of this fascinating means of construction it is worth comparing traditional reinforced concrete with prestressed concrete.

The strength of a simple reinforced concrete beam depends for its stability on the fact that steel rods, placed in the bottom of the beam, as far as possible from the neutral axis, resist the tensile forces without any help from the concrete. The compressive forces in the top of the beam are resisted by the compressive strength of the concrete without any help from the steel. The two stresses, compression at

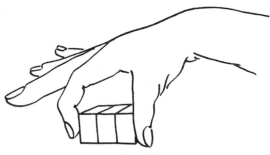

FIG. 159

the top and tension at the bottom, must be equal, otherwise the molecules of the beam would part company. The foregoing is a very simplified statement of the structural mechanics involved in ordinary reinforced concrete, but will suffice for the purpose of comparison.

The strength of a simple prestressed concrete beam depends for its stability on the fact that concrete is an excellent material to withstand compression, and that *the whole section of the beam* can be used for compression, without throwing away, as it were, that portion of the beam lying beneath the neutral axis.

The steel in a prestressed beam is not used to take the load in tension, but its function is rather that of a giant binding wire to keep the imaginary segments or voussoirs of the beam from falling apart.

As a simple experiment, cut three or four neat 1in. slices off a piece of timber, say $1\frac{1}{2}$in. × $1\frac{1}{2}$in., and grip them as tightly as possible between thumb and forefinger, as shown in Fig. 159. It at

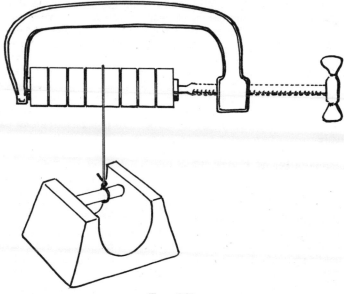

Fig. 160

once becomes apparent that the small beam in slices has no strength in its loose state, and yet, the harder it is clasped, would support quite a load without falling apart. Carrying the experiment a stage further, as in Fig. 160, take sufficient segments of the small beam to form a miniature lintol, say 6in. long, place them very carefully together in as true an alignment as possible, and screw up firmly in a

Q

G cramp. It will be found that the lintol will support a heavy concentrated load at the weakest point, namely, the centre, and *over a joint*, without collapsing. Slowly release the G cramp and the lintol collapses. These two experiments demonstrate the whole simple theory of prestressed concrete. Simple as the theory is, to carry it out in practice is extremely complicated and involved, demanding an expert knowledge of mathematics, physics, and structural mechanics, so do not be misled by the simplicity of the main idea!

By inserting the segments of a small beam into a carpenter's G cramp and screwing up tightly, we have put the whole of the fibres in the lintol into compression to such an extent that the natural tendency of the segments to slide past each other has been overcome.

It will be objected that a concrete beam which is cast in one piece has no joints as shown in the illustration. That is quite true; and yet the joints are there, or rather, they *want* to be there! Any beam, in whatever material it is made, may be considered to consist of separate segments as close together as we choose to imagine them. The action of the various forces on a girder produced by the dead and live loads tends to divide the girder into portions all along its length.

From theorising on a small scale to actual practice, where it is a question of beams, bridges, huge stanchions, or dam walls, we are confronted by the fact that concrete used in vast quantities, over long spans and in great depth, cannot be compressed by means of a carpenter's G cramp. Some other means must be found to provide the enormous force necessary.

A means *has* been found in high tensile steel wires or cables. Whereas ordinary mild steel bars for general reinforcing work have a tensile strength of 28 to 32 tons/in.^{2}, high tensile steel, as used in prestressed concrete, has an ultimate tensile strength of 90 to 120 tons/in.^{2}, according to the diameter of the wires.

Fig. 161 shows a much exaggerated drawing of a piece of steel wire. A is the original length divided into twelve equal imaginary sections, the last two portions being sub-divided into two and four equal parts. B represents the same piece of wire elongated under tension, produced either by hanging a very heavy weight on the wire, pulling out in a machine, or by means of hydraulic jacks. Two things will be noticed.

(*a*) As the wire is stretched, so the cross-sectional diameter becomes smaller. This diminution takes place equally all along the line.

(*b*) Each of the imaginary 12 equal divisions in A become elongated into 12 equal divisions in B. The wire does not stretch excessively thin in some places and hardly at all in others, as suggested in C.

It is this unique property of high tensile steel wire which is made use of in prestressed concrete, instead of the elementary G cramp, to supply the tremendous compressive forces at the ends of the beams.

Once again we have to thank those wonderful people of the 17th and 18th centuries for benefits bestowed on future generations. It was Doctor Robert Hooke (1635–1733), an English mathematician

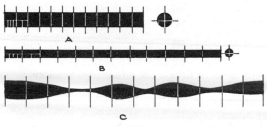

FIG. 161

and Professor of Geometry at Gresham College, who formulated what has come to be known as Hooke's Law. This Law defines the properties and measurement of elasticity for various materials used in our modern manufactures and constructions. Doctor Robert Hooke discovered that, within certain limits, stress is directly proportional to strain. A stress of so many tons per sq. in. on a piece of steel wire will produce an elongation in that wire exactly proportional to the force employed. A load of 10 tons suspended from a piece of steel wire will elongate the wire twice as much as a load of 5 tons. The length of the elongation can be measured and compared with its original length. The percentage of increase in length so obtained will always be the same for the material, according to the force employed and the cross-sectional area. There is, however, a limit, beyond which steel will not go without snapping or becoming permanently deformed, or even producing some of the effects shown in Fig. 161 c. This point is known as the elastic limit.

Steel also possesses to a marked degree the quality of retracting to its original length before it was stretched, and in so doing, exerting the same force that was used to stretch it. If a force of 10 tons per sq. in. was exerted on a piece of steel and then relaxed, the steel would in turn exert a force of 10 tons in returning to the original length; if the force were 50 tons per sq. in., the steel would reciprocate with 50 tons on being released.

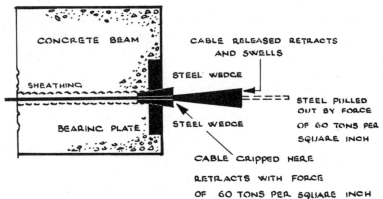

FIG. 162

Fig. 162 gives a purely diagrammatic sketch of a high tensile cable which has been stressed to 60 tons per sq. in. by a jack and wedged against a bearing plate to prevent the cable from contracting to its original length. The action as portrayed in the diagram is highly exaggerated. It will be noticed how the steel cable, being prevented by the wedges from regaining its original length and diameter, tends to swell at the free end, thereby increasing the security of the wedges.

Having briefly outlined the aims and general workings of prestressed concrete it will now be possible to investigate an actual design.

Assume a concrete beam of 20ft. 0in. span, say 12in. deep and 5in. wide, which is required to support a uniformly distributed load of 125lb./ft. run including its own weight (Fig. 163).

Concrete (1–2–4) crushing strength at 28 days   5,500lb.
Working stress   1,350lb.
Distributed load   2,500lb.

Bending moment $\dfrac{125 \times 20^2}{8}$ = 6,250lb. ft.

$$= 75,000\text{lb. in.}$$

Section modulus $\dfrac{Bd^2}{6} = \dfrac{5 \times 12 \times 12}{6}$ = 120in.^{3}

Stress on cross-sectional area of 5in. × 12in. beam

$$\frac{75,000}{120} = 625\text{lb./in.}^2$$

The stress diagram for the beam is as in Fig. 163. Engineers find it convenient to denote compression by a + (plus) sign and tension by a − (minus) sign, so that the top half of the diagram has a + index, whilst the bottom carries a − index.

Looking at the diagram it will be seen that although the concrete in compression is only stressed to 625lb./in.^{2}, it could safely support a stress of 1,350lb./in.^{2}. On the other hand (according to our previous knowledge of reinforced concrete), the bottom half in tension requires the aid of steel bars to withstand the strain. For all practical purposes concrete has no tensile strength.

Several very clever engineers, chief amongst them being M. Eugene Freyssinet in France and Professor Gustave Magnel in Belgium, spotted this problem, finally evolving the ingenious system of pre-stressing, to overcome the lack of tensile strength in the concrete.

Refer once more to Fig. 162 and apply it to the present problem. Let us suppose that a steel cable has been passed clean through the centre of the concrete beam, stretched by means of powerful hydraulic jacks, and wedged up tight, so that it induces a compressive stress in the whole of the section of 625lb./in.^{2} (Fig. 165). The area has been shown solid black to denote that it is prestress.

Place Fig. 166 (a simple repeat of the stress diagram, Fig. 164) by the side of the solid black diagram, then superimpose them, as in Fig. 167. It will at once jump to the eye that an extremely clever thing has been brought about.

(a) The compressive stress in the concrete has been increased to 1,250lb./in.^{2}, well under the allowable stress of 1,350lb./in.^{2}.

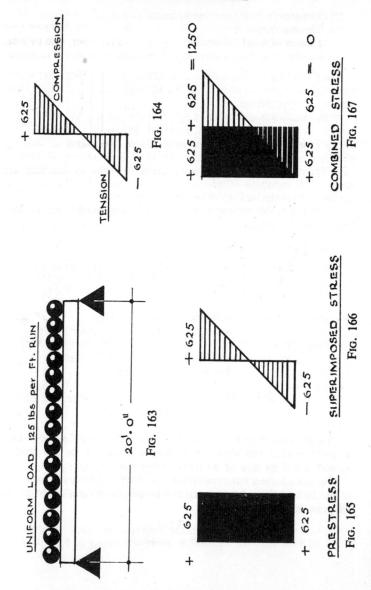

UNIFORM LOAD 125 lbs per Ft. RUN

20' 0"

FIG. 163

COMPRESSION

+ 625

− 625

TENSION

FIG. 164

625

+ 625

PRESTRESS

FIG. 165

+ 625

− 625

SUPERIMPOSED STRESS

FIG. 166

+ 625 + 625 = 1250

+ 625 − 625 = 0

COMBINED STRESS

FIG. 167

(*b*) The tensile stress has been cancelled out.
(*c*) The above manœuvre has virtually transformed the beam into a series of short columns tightly packed together, side by side, so that it is only a question of compression in the concrete.

The foregoing explanation is exceedingly hypothetical and would require many qualifications, but it gives a good idea of the physical action of prestressing.

Wires used for prestressing are mostly ·20in. and ·276in. diameter. It has been found that wires of this small cross-section are much more reliable in manufacture from the point of view of ductility and all-round quality of production, evenness of temper, etc. They can be coiled into large-diameter coils so that they are easy to transport to a job, and such wire can also be paid out straight from the coil without straightening.

To return to the problem. If the beam is stressed to 625lb./in.², the following results:

$$5 \times 12 \times 625\text{lb.} = 37,500\text{lb.}$$

There is thus a force of 37,500lb. tending to open up the joints as indicated in the highly exaggerated Fig. 168.

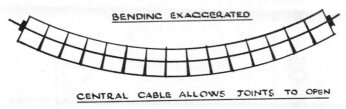

FIG. 168

The obvious thing to do is to tighten up the central cable in such a manner that the stress of 37,500lb. produced by the load is counteracted by one of 37,500lb. produced by the cable.

High tensile steel has a conservative strength of 90 to 100 tons/in.². It would be safe and good practice to assume a tensile strength of 65 tons/in.².

$$\frac{37,500}{65 \times 2,240}$$

$$\text{Log } 37500 \qquad\qquad = 4\cdot5740$$
$$\text{Log} \qquad 65 = 1\cdot8129$$
$$\text{Log} \quad 2240 = 3\cdot3502$$

$$\qquad\qquad\qquad 5\cdot1631 \qquad 5\cdot1631$$

$$\qquad\qquad\qquad\qquad\qquad -1\cdot4109$$

Anti log $-1\cdot4109 = \cdot2575$in.^{2} (area of steel required)

Choose an even number of wires $\cdot20$in. in diameter, $\cdot0314$in. sectional area.

$$\frac{\cdot2575}{\cdot0314} = \text{number of wires}$$
$$\text{Log } \cdot2575 = -1\cdot4108$$
$$\text{Log } \cdot0314 = -2\cdot4969$$

$$\qquad\qquad\qquad\quad \cdot9139$$

Anti log $\cdot9139 = 8\cdot202$ (say 10 wires)

An engineer in actual practice would make a choice between 8 and 10 wires.

The next thing to determine is the permanent tension to apply in order to achieve the above results. This calculation is easy.

$$\frac{37,500}{2,240 \times 10(\cdot0314)} = \frac{37,500}{2,240 \times \cdot314}$$
$$\text{Log } 37,000 \qquad\qquad = 4\cdot5740$$
$$\text{Log} \quad 2,240 = \qquad 3\cdot3502$$
$$\text{Log} \qquad \cdot314 = -1\cdot4969$$

$$\qquad\qquad\qquad 2\cdot8471 \quad = 2\cdot8471$$

$$\qquad\qquad\qquad\qquad\qquad 1\cdot7269$$

Anti log $1\cdot7269 = 53\cdot32$ tons
(say) 54 tons

So far, so good, in theory. In practice an extra allowance of 10 tons would have to be added to the jack reading to compensate for various losses. Concrete shrinks, steel itself relaxes its tension, anchorages are imperfect, wedges slip, jacks and gauges do not always register correctly, unexplained differences occur between the calculated extension on the wires and the force applied.

The total force to be applied in this case would therefore be 64 tons.

A great improvement on the central cable is obtained by passing the steel wires through the lower portion of the beam, so that they are eccentric to the neutral axis (Fig. 169). This method enables a

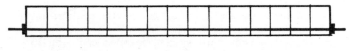

ECCENTRIC CABLE KEEPS JOINTS CLOSED

Fig. 169

much heavier superimposed load to be carried *without increasing the size of the concrete beam*. As will be seen from the diagram, one of the consequences is to close the imaginary joints which are striving to open under pressure.

It may be repeated that the joints do not actually exist in the beam, but that they are indeed virtually present is demonstrated by the fact that a prestressed beam which is overloaded opens up all the way. Immediately the overload is removed, the cracks disappear, and the beam is as good as ever, both in appearance and structural soundness.

Even further refinements can be effected by bowing the cable. The calculations are involved and would take us too deeply into the subject to warrant dealing with here. .

There are five chief systems of prestressing in general use, each with its variant, and bearing the name of the inventor or company exploiting it.

    (*a*) The Freyssinet
    (*b*) The Magnel-Blaton
    (*c*) The Lee-McCall
    (*d*) The Gifford-Udall (CCL)
    (*e*) The S.D.L.

All systems are essentially composed of wires, single, grouped, or stranded, or even solid bars. The cables are all of high tensile steel with a tensile strength of between 90 to 120 tons/in.² With wires of very small diameter it is possible to obtain a tensile strength of 150 tons/in.² With the cables or tendons go certain components to anchor the ends of the wires and to spread the compressive stress over the ends of the beam. The following brief table lists what will be required to construct a prestressed beam. Not all these components will be necessary in one beam, of course.

(a) Wires from ·104in. up to ·276in. made up in cores from 6 to 12 wires per core.

(b) Variants of the above but spliced or stranded to form ropes from ½in. to 1⅛in. diameter.

(c) Alloy steel rods with special threaded ends ½in. to 1⅛in. diameter.

(d) Light metal sheathing of all diameters to cover the cables and protect them from contact with the concrete. The sheathing is very carefully fixed and positioned in the formwork before the beams are cast, especially in the case of a bowed cable, where it is an essential part of the engineer's design to fix the cables to the exact profile of the drawings.

(e) Heavy steel anchor and bearing plates with a system of steel wedges to anchor the cable firmly as shown in diagrammatic form (Fig. 162). It must be emphasised that Fig. 162 is not intended to be a diagram of any particular system.

(f) Suitable spacers to form a core for the wires and to keep them from getting crossed whilst being threaded through the beam. The spacers are either metal or plastic. Single-rod cables do not need spacers.

(g) Hydraulic jack, together with pump capable of exerting pressures from 5 to 100 tons, together with various adapters to take from 1 to 12 wires at a time (Fig. 170).

(h) Power-operated grout pump for cementing the cables inside the ducts after stressing is completed and the wedges driven home.

There are two cases where steel wedges are not used to anchor the cables. The Freyssinet system has a very ingenious device consisting of a cast concrete tube lined with high tensile steel wire and a cast concrete wedge, conical in form, grooved for 8 to 12 wires or more. The cast concrete tube is set in the end of the beam, the cable threaded through, the concrete grooved wedge is inserted and then driven home by the same jack that was used for tensioning (Fig. 171).

The Lee-McCall system has a thread formed on the ends of the bar and is secured by washers and nuts after tension has been

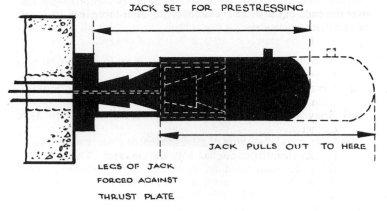

JACK SET FOR PRESTRESSING

JACK PULLS OUT TO HERE

LEGS OF JACK
FORCED AGAINST
THRUST PLATE

FIG. 170

CONCRETE GROOVED
CONE GRIPS WIRES
RAMMED HOME BY
HYDRAULIC JACK

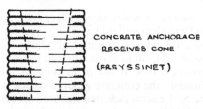

GROUT CONDUIT

CONCRETE ANCHORAGE
RECEIVES CONE

(FREYSSINET)

FIG. 171

applied. This system has the added advantage that prestressing can be carried out in stages and released if necessary, or the entire beam can be entirely restressed (Fig. 172).

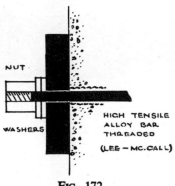

NUT

WASHERS

HIGH TENSILE
ALLOY BAR
THREADED

(LEE – MC.CALL)

Fig. 172

INDEX